The
Horse Lover's Guide
to Massage

What Your Horse Wants You to Know

ALL ABOUT
Animal
Massage
SERIES

The Horse Lover's Guide to Massage

What Your Horse Wants You to Know

Megan Ayrault, LMP, L/SAMP

Licensed Massage Practitioner
Large and Small Animal Massage Practitioner

www.AllAboutAnimalMassage.com

This book is intended for animal owners and caregivers to learn information and skills that will complement care from professionals, including from veterinarians. It is not intended as a substitute for veterinary advice, diagnosis, or treatment. Animal owners should consult their veterinarian regularly, including in regard to any symptoms that may require diagnosis or treatment.

Any animal handling, including massage and bodywork, holds the potential for harm to handler, animal, or both. The author and her associates offer important safety guidelines, but assume no liability for how the information in this book, or in the other resources at *www.AllAboutAnimalMassage.com*, is implemented.

Published by
All About Animal Massage
PO Box 56, Kirkland, Washington 98083
www.AllAboutAnimalMassage.com

First Edition

Edited and packaged by CeciBooks Editorial & Publishing
Cover and interior design by Karen Johnson, Level 29 Design
Photographs by Ann Chase Photography
Illustrations by Margo McKnight, ©The Northwest School of Animal Massage

Library of Congress Cataloging-in-Publication Data
Ayrault, Megan
The horse lover's guide to massage: what your horse wants you to know / by Megan Ayrault.
ISBN: 978-0-9822556-1-2

1. Horses—Disease—Alternative Treatment 2. Animal Massage 3. Complementary Care 4. Title

Dedication

If you love someone,
the greatest gift you can give them
is your true presence.

Thich Nhat Hanh

Our animals generously offer us this gift every day. How often do we truly receive it? Or return it? Could we learn to do better?

This seemingly simple act of offering our true presence, as well as receiving another's, is at the heart of all bodywork, including massage.

I'm grateful to my many animal and human teachers, including colleagues, clients, students, friends, and family. Your support has been generous in many ways, and you continue to teach me about true presence every day. It is a vital lesson, among many, in the art and science of doing bodywork; one that I will always appreciate opportunities to practice.

Contents

Introduction

This book is about more than just horse massage. True, it is about horses' bodies and specifically the many ways they respond to massage. More importantly though, it is about deepening your connectedness with the horses in your life by learning more about what is going on under their skin, and discovering the powerful tool of massage for their physical and emotional health. The process of learning to better care for our animals is never-ending, and this book, along with my other books and website, *www.AllAboutAnimalMassage.com*, is intended to be an important part of that process for you. I also hope that through your love for horses and your motivation to learn more about caring for them, you will learn more about how your own body works (because it's much the same), and how to better care for yourself as well. As you read this book you will find information, therapeutic techniques, insights, resources, and inspiration for all of these purposes.

Massage for people and now also for animals is becoming more mainstream every passing year as the many benefits are experienced and recognized. Horse owners everywhere are learning how massage and bodywork can contribute significantly to ease of movement, health, and quality of life for their horses. Of course this is in addition to the regular care from your horse's veterinarian. After reading this book you will not only be able to massage your horse, but you will understand exactly what each technique is doing, how the body is benefiting, and how massage works.

Part one of this book, "A Consumer's Guide to Horse Massage," focuses on two topics. The first and most fascinating one is how your horse's body responds to outside influences, whether adapting to the effects of stress and trauma or healing in response to therapies like massage. This information will give you new and deeper insights into what's going on under your horse's skin, which will enhance your awareness of your horse's needs and the effectiveness of your massage. The second focus is professional massage; it provides information that can help you find and work with an animal massage therapist or bodyworker to support your horse's optimal health and well-being. Both topics together will make you a more savvy and educated receiver of massage, whether for your horse or for yourself.

Part two is the how-to portion: "Massaging Your Horse." You will learn massage techniques that will help you monitor, support, and learn about your horse's body. I have included suggestions on variations of the techniques, and coaching tips to make the quality of your touch more therapeutic as you practice over time. Along with each technique, you will also learn something about your horse's anatomy that relates to that technique. You can use this anatomy information to help you visualize and focus as you massage, enhancing the results for your horse and the fun for yourself.

Parts one and two of this book are designed to work synergistically. That is, by reading either part alone you will learn a lot and help your horse, but if you read and use both parts together, the effect will be more than double. In addition to being a great resource on its own, this book is also part of a larger whole. It is interconnected with its partner website, *www. AllAboutAnimalMassage.com*, where you will find many additional resources, including a panel of Expert Advisors, the free "All About Animal Massage" newsletter, articles, videos, photos, e-books, shared stories and testimonials, training, recommended books, DVDs and other products, and links to further resources, all to continue your education and inspiration into the future. Last but not least you will find the "Animal Wellness Network," where animal lovers of all backgrounds and levels of expertise can find, support, and learn from each other for the benefit of all animals. Whether or not you choose to actively participate and create your own profile in this network, you can always use it to search for animal care professionals near you, including massage and bodywork professionals.

Among many books available in the website's store is this book's companion e-book, *Massaging My Horse: A Guided Journal,* an interactive workbook that will lead you through the learning process of "Massaging Your Horse," part two of this book.

The journal includes:

• Additional information and guidance on assessing your horse's body and reading his feedback

• Charts and instructions to record your massages

Completing the journal and the charts will help you identify patterns of tension in your horse's body and show the progress you both make together over time.

These guided journals make ideal educational projects for young people, too, including those involved with organizations such as 4-H, Pony Club, or Scouts.

For any dog lovers you know (perhaps yourself?), *The Dog Lover's Guide to Massage: What Your Dog Wants You to Know* is a valuable addition to their dog library. Most of the techniques and anatomy taught in *The Dog Lover's Guide* are different from what you will find here for horses, yet the information can be easily adapted to the other species with a few adjustments.

If you don't have a need for the dog book yourself, you can still get the additional massage techniques and anatomy information by purchasing the supplemental e-book *More Massage Moves for Horse Lovers,* which contains the techniques and anatomy taught in *The Dog Lover's Guide* already adapted for horses.

Finally, on the website you will find the free e-book *Animal Massage: A Consumer Guide,* which is less extensive than part one of this book, but also includes a few things this book does not. I hope you will take a look at it for yourself, and also refer other animal lovers to it for an easy, accessible, and free introduction to animal massage.

Part One

A Consumer's Guide to Horse Massage

It's easy to provide your horse with many of the benefits massage has to offer.

I

Loving Your Horse with Massage: The Benefits

Picture a foal at play in a field. See in your mind's eye how fully his whole body participates in every movement. What are some words that come to mind? Joy, energy, exuberance, fluidity, ease, fun!

Now picture the same horse a bit older, then much older. What are the qualities of his movement now? Of course, the inner spirit may still share all the qualities described above and more, but for now, just consider how he is *moving.* How do you sense he is feeling physically? Is it really only age that's making the difference?

Perhaps you know an older person who is devoted to an activity such as dance, yoga, or a martial art—an activity that promotes both strength and flexibility equally throughout the whole body. How does this person move? Do words like ease, fluidity, and joy come to mind more easily than when you visualized the older horse?

Well, this book is about massage, not dance, yoga, or martial arts, but what do they have in common? Health and vitality, or in other words, joy, energy, exuberance, fluidity, ease, and fun. A lifetime of healthy exercise would certainly promote all of these, but most of our horses, like most of us, spend too much time not moving much at all, moving in limited, habitual patterns, or moving in ways that are more stressful to the body than healthful. Fortunately, there is another means of creating some of the important benefits that exercise gives us and a few additional ones: massage! Massage does far more than ease sore muscles. What is actually going on under the skin? How is the body responding and changing?

We all know that massage relieves sore muscles and provides some well-deserved pampering. Here are some examples of additional benefits received from massage.

- Boosts the immune system

- Improves the quality and symmetry of movement

- Balances muscle tone for better joint health and function

- Promotes earlier detection of stresses and strains

- Stimulates circulation for greater health of all tissues

- Helps reduce risk, severity, and frequency of injuries

- Improves athletic agility and coordination

- Promotes strength and endurance

- Reduces the effects of stress

- Minimizes restrictions caused by old scar tissue

- Promotes the development of more functional scar tissue during healing

- Reduces or eliminates adhesions, knots, and other restrictions

- Improves skeletal alignment and posture for more efficient movement

- Releases endorphins (natural "feel good" painkillers)

- Lowers blood pressure

- Improves digestion

- Supports recovery from injury, surgery, or other traumas

- Reduces swelling

- Optimizes the training and learning progress due to better health, calmer mind, and greater body awareness and comfort

- Improves the quality of sleep

- Releases stored toxins

- Increases flexibility and resilience

- Deepens your relationship with your animal

How does massage do all that, you might ask? In chapter 3 you will learn six concepts about how bodies work, your horse's and your own. Each concept will be explained in a way that shows clearly *how* various types of bodywork and massage can lead to these significant benefits. That is, any one of the six could be all it takes to make you say, "Wow, massage is cool!" but I'll go through all six anyway to further enlighten you. That way you will also have a good sense of why so many different types of massage all work, just in different ways. You will also see that even if a massage session does not provide the specific result you were looking for, that doesn't mean nothing therapeutic happened.

In fact, this brings me to an important point about interpreting results of massage. Some benefits, such as "improves the quality and symmetry of movement," can often be readily seen following a massage or felt by a rider. But let's take an example like "helps reduce risk, severity, and frequency of injuries." It can be difficult at best to prove results such as this one because you can't know how your horse would have fared had he *not* received a massage. For example, say you have a professional massage for your horse, and a few days later he's lame.

Does that mean the massage did no good? Not at all. Perhaps rather than a torn muscle, for example, your horse has now only strained it, possibly thanks to the massage having reduced at least some of the stresses that had been building over time.

We can't prove or disprove such scenarios, but what we can do is look at the physiology of the muscles and other soft tissues; that is, how they work and how massage affects them. Muscles, tendons, and ligaments, for example, are all more prone to injury when muscles are fatigued. Muscles are more prone to fatigue when they are chronically tight and the tissue is less resilient, which can happen for many reasons, as discussed in chapter 2. Chapters 3 and 4 will give you information on how the body responds both to stress and to massage, which will better enable you to understand the many benefits of massage. And if you visit *www.AllAboutAnimalMassage.com*, you will find shared stories and observations about the results of massage and bodywork that people have witnessed in their animal companions.

How Does Massage Resemble Car Maintenance?

In this section I'm going to use a machine analogy for the body, but please don't take this to mean that bodies are actually very machine-like. They most definitely are not, neither ours nor our horses. Too bad for our cars. If they were more like our animals, maybe they could also adapt and compensate, limping along at least enough to get us to the service station when something goes wrong. Wouldn't that be helpful?

Even though living bodies are much more than merely complicated machines, there is at least one comparison that relates very well to massage. Car maintenance. This is the idea that sometimes it's wise to take action to prevent a problem, rather than waiting until something breaks down. Yes, you can definitely save money in the short run by not getting oil changes, or new tires, filters, brake pads, etc. But is that really smart? Of course even if you get the regular service, there's no guarantee your car won't eventually have a problem, but it is likely that over the lifetime of your car you will have fewer and less costly repairs if you invest in maintenance.

So what is optimal maintenance for your horse's body? Even a car's performance is not totally predictable, let alone a living body's. But you can figure that certain factors will influence how much maintenance a car requires, and also what the odds are that it may also need repairs sooner than later. For a car, these factors include mileage, types of road surfaces, speeds driven, accidents, quality of fuel, condition of tires, and of course the quality of the car to start with (conformation), not to mention whether it's being used for the type of driving for which it was actually designed.

See anything in this list you recognize for your horse? I hope you also see that this analogy applies not only to massage but also to how a horse is exercised and handled, the quality of food, conformation, regular veterinary care of course, and so on. The more challenges your horse has to his body, the more massage can support him.

In this car maintenance analogy, waiting until your horse is injured or obviously in pain before using massage is like waiting for your car to break down in traffic before you ever take it to a mechanic. One significant difference, though, is that your horse is a living being that has been experiencing, except in cases of sudden injury or illness, a gradual onset of symptoms while you were either waiting for them to go away or not paying attention. I know I've made this mistake myself with my own horses, and I'm a massage therapist!

My point is not to add to any feelings of guilt but just to offer an important reminder for our horses' sakes. Learning the information in this book will raise the bar of your responsibility to your animals, but only because it will also raise your awareness and your skills to detect the needs of your horse's body sooner than you have been able to in the past. To get back to our analogy, this is just like the way a more experienced and knowledgeable driver is more able and likely to notice early warning signs of trouble in a car's engine and provide the appropriate care right away.

As you may have already noticed, I sometimes refer to "bodywork" instead of always using the term massage. While the many varieties of massage are types of bodywork, not all bodywork is massage. Here are just a few examples to illustrate the range of bodywork. It can include Sports Massage, Lymphatic Facilitation, Deep Tissue Massage, Acupressure, Shiatsu, Myofascial Release, Craniosacral Therapy, Structural Integration, Rolfing, Trigger Point Therapy, Neuromuscular Therapy, Reflexology, and many, many more. Not to mention new ones being developed almost every day, it seems! Modalities (types of bodywork) may focus on muscles, skeletal alignment, internal organs, the rhythm and flow of cerebral-spinal fluid, the balance of Chi energy in meridian pathways, the stimulation of the lymphatic system, and so on. The information in this book, though its focus is massage, applies to virtually all forms of bodywork. This is because it's about the body, and about various effects therapeutic touch can have on the body, and how those effects happen. You can find out more about varieties of massage and bodywork, or a specific modality, at *www.AllAboutAnimalMassage.com*.

2

Why and When
Horses Need Massage

Horses in our society often experience phenomenal support, care, and love in many ways. The growing interest in complementary services like massage is a wonderful testimonial to this fact. Yet all horses, even the ones we go to great lengths to care for, also face certain challenges to their health and comfort.

As you read the following examples of stress factors for horses, imagine how each situation might be impacting your own horse's body and health. When you read the next chapter, "How Massage Works," you will find information about your horse's physiology (that is, how the body functions) that will give you more ideas and clearer pictures of what is going on under the skin, first in response to stress, and then in response to massage.

Stress Factors

Lack of movement: This may be due to stall rest while recovering from an injury, or even just the typical stall living in which many horses are kept. It can also be due to more temporary confinement, such as a long trailer ride (which creates even more stresses than confinement). Even horses who are turned out in dirt paddocks will often spend most of the day standing if they don't have access to grazing or other horses to encourage activity. Contrast this with horses in nature, who spend much of their day covering many miles as they graze and socialize. (Lack of social interaction can be just as stressful as lack of movement.)

Injuries: Repetitive stress injuries and trauma are the main categories. Keep in mind that any surgery certainly counts as trauma from which your horse must heal, even if the surgery also produces therapeutic results in the long term. However an injury occurs, it brings on a cascade of additional stresses to deal with, starting with the fact that the rest of the body compensates for the injured area in order to protect it. Often the hours spent confined will be increased and exercise decreased. Pain and confinement will make sleep less restful and decrease gut activity. Medications may stress the organs in a variety of ways.

Pulls on leadropes, reins, martingales, etc.: These pressures may be initiated by either the horse or a human, but either way the horse's body has forces to resist. These pressures may seem minor, almost unnoticeable, yet they occur frequently enough to have cumulative effects; for example, a rider continually hangs on one or both reins, or the horse braces against a martingale. At other times the forces may be much more traumatic and sudden, as when a frightened horse pulls back and breaks a rope she's tied with. In either case, whether or not the injury is obvious right away, it can easily result in problems days, weeks, and even years later.

Riders: Starting with the process of getting on, putting all your weight in one stirrup even briefly during mounting or dismounting pulls the horse's back vertebrae to one side. Repeated over time, this can cause significant trouble for the back, and therefore the whole body. Using a mounting block and alternating the side you mount from are excellent ways to minimize the negative effects for your horse, and also, with practice, to get your own body better balanced. Once mounted, the more unbalanced the rider, the greater the impact for the horse. Even the most balanced rider, however, will have at least *some* subtle asymmetries in his or her own body; perhaps a stronger and weaker side, or one hip or shoulder higher or lower. In addition to this, the fact is that our horses feel and are affected by the patterns and areas of tension we each hold in our bodies. That said, the most skilled riders (a select group) certainly do the horses they ride far more good than harm, as they are able to minimize the negative impact of their own imbalances while maximizing positive influences that actually help the horse become *more* balanced. There is always more to learn about the art of riding in such a way that it actually benefits your horse's body, and she will be the first to appreciate your efforts.

Poorly fitting saddles: A delicate subject, to say the least, which also extends to girth and pad issues (as well as bridles, blankets, boots; really, anything attached to a horse's body).

Take a look at several horses' backs, and you will quickly see that there is as much variety in shape as there is when comparing their bodies as a whole. The differences are much more extensive than mere size. Suppose you measure the size of your feet, even specifying how wide. Can you expect to be comfortable in every pair of shoes you order in that size and width? Of course not. And does wearing a good pair of socks make up for tight spots? Hardly.

Know that pressure damage to muscle and other soft tissues happens deep under the skin *before* it appears at the surface. Many stoic and tolerant horses spend a lifetime putting up with unnecessary pain and dysfunction without their riders ever realizing. For more on this important topic, please visit *www.AllAboutAnimalMassage.com*.

Imagine for yourself the impacts of these additional stress factors:

- Activities that push your horse's ability, fitness, or conformation to the limits. This is not all bad, as appropriate challenges are what make us stronger, but pushing limits does carry the risk of excess stress and injury.

- Long or poorly trimmed hooves that unbalance the joints of the foot and leg.

- Emotional stresses that impact the body in many ways, such as affecting the breath, immune system, nervous system, muscle tension, and so on.

- Allergies, excessive bug bites, poorly fitting blankets that rub, and anything that creates inflammation followed by adhesions (gluing) between the skin and underlying tissues.

This list is not complete, but you get the idea. Massage can help recovery from or management of these various stresses by stimulating circulation, easing and balancing muscle tensions, breaking up adhesions, calming nerves—just to name a few examples. The results you can expect will vary depending on many factors, but typically owners who use massage for their horses are thrilled with the outcome. Am I saying that massage is a magic cure? Of course not—though it can sometimes seem, and even be, miraculous. More often it's the smaller miracles, the ones that may even go unnoticed at first, but that add up over time, such as breathing a little more deeply, a more even flow of movement through the hips and tail, standing more square and straight, or lying down to sleep more.

Massage Is Complementary to Chiropractic Care

Another great benefit of massage is helping chiropractic adjustments hold better, hold longer, and even happen more easily in the first place. Horses may need chiropractic care for all the same reasons they need massage. In fact, it can often be an imbalance of muscle tensions over time that creates chiropractic subluxations ("stuckness" of joints impacting surrounding nerves and tissues). Other causes include pulling back on ropes, falls, knocking a hip in a gateway, kicks from other horses, and rider influences. It is beyond the scope of this book to cover tips on working with a chiropractor, but it is an important and very related topic, so please visit *www.AllAboutAnimalMassage.com* for more information. For now I can only say please choose your horse's chiropractor with special care and attention, since chiropractic adjustments include greater risk of harm than massage if performed by someone not skilled and knowledgeable about both chiropractic care and horse anatomy and health.

For situations when massage is not appropriate (contraindications) see chapter 6: "Guidelines for Effectiveness and Safety," and the website *www.AllAboutAnimalMassage.com*.

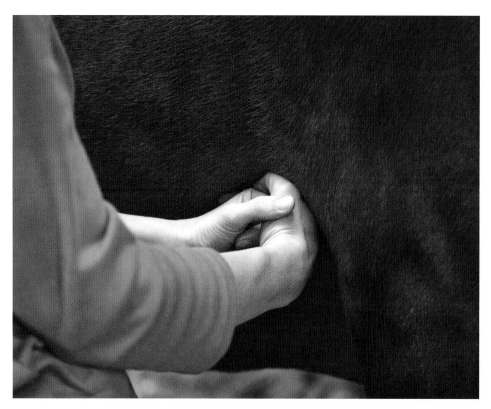

Understanding what is happening for your horse's body will help you apply techniques more effectively.

3
How Massage Works

In chapter 2 we considered a number of stress factors that can affect your horse. Could you see how each of them might have a profound effect on your horse's body? Now read on, and see how the following six concepts can add to what you already know.

Freeing Restrictions: Muscles and Other Soft Tissues

Concept 1: Glue—or Restrictions, Adhesions, Knots, and Trigger Points

Two things that happen throughout all bodies at different times, a little here, a lot there, are inflammation and dehydration. Inflammation could be as obvious as a swollen injury, or more invisible like sore, achy muscles after a workout. Dehydration might affect the whole system due to not drinking enough water, but even more often will involve a smaller area of tissue that's simply not getting a good supply of fluids, including water, because of tensions, scar tissue, or other restrictions. Inflammation and dehydration both cause the surrounding muscle and other tissues to become less slippery and more sticky. Not only that, but once they start to get sticky, they're also more prone to *(drum roll)* dehydration and inflammation!

As adhesions and restrictions develop, muscles shorten, become even more dehydrated and acidic, develop trigger points and stress points, and generally become dysfunctional. This means they get tired more easily, if they even function properly in the first place. Muscle fatigue and tension, in turn, put extra strain on the tendons and ligaments. Restrictions also create more stress for other structures both near and far, as they work harder trying to compensate and rebalance the body. These other structures may manage to compensate well for a long time, even a lifetime. However, there will always be a price paid at some level eventually, whether as injury, pain, lower energy, less coordination, loss of flexibility, lower endurance, and so on. The good news is that massage is excellent at rehydrating, unsticking, and reducing pain in restrictions such as adhesions and trigger points, whether or not they've yet resulted in a palpable knot.

Relieving Stress: Neurological Effects

Concept 2: Fight or Flight versus Rest and Relaxation

Stress is quite the buzzword these days, and for very good reason. It is well worth paying attention to, but without stressing about it, of course! First, take a deep breath. Relax. The good news is that our bodies are well designed to handle stress. In fact, too little stress can be just as much of a problem as too much. Healthy stress stimulates our bodies to become stronger, but only if relaxation and recovery are also part of the picture.

Our central nervous system (brain and spinal cord) coordinates activities and sensations throughout our body. Much of this happens without our even thinking about it, such as the regulation of heart rate and blood pressure. Since there are times we need these rates to be high and other times when we don't, the automatic part of our nervous system has two modes that correspond to our different needs: fight or flight and rest and relaxation. The technical terms for these are the *sympathetic* (fight or flight) and the *parasympathetic* (rest and relaxation) systems.

Sympathetic mode is about survival in the short term. In its extreme, it is about saving ourselves from the saber-toothed tiger (or trailers, whips, plastic bags, fireworks, fill-in-the-blank) right *now*. In the less extreme version, it is about anticipating and avoiding the scary or worrisome things in life. Chronic stress means being constantly in this low to moderate state of alarm or worry. Like a broken record, we get in a certain groove and our bodies literally get stuck there, forgetting how to get back into relaxation mode even when we do take a break. This can be as true for animals as it is for us, particularly if *we* are in this pattern, as they take so many of their cues from the humans in their lives.

Our bodies are designed to work with a *balance* of the two systems. The sympathetic mode is highly useful when we need a burst of strength or activity, but having our bodies revved up all the time would (and often does) wear them out faster than necessary. If we haven't had a chance to really rest, relax, and recover, there will be less energy available for those moments when we really need it.

Great news! Positive touch stimulates the parasympathetic *(para-sym-pa-thet-ic)* nervous system, the rest and relaxation mode. When do you think your body would choose to work on a healing process—while the tiger is chasing you or while you're relaxing? Yes, the physiological processes (in other words, activities of the cells, organs, glands, etc.) that promote healing are stimulated in the parasympathetic state. Examples of the rest and relaxation mode include the following: the heart rate slows; blood vessels dilate (enlarge), which allows better distribution of nutrients; the breath deepens, bringing more oxygen to the blood; waste products and toxins are removed more efficiently; and endorphins (natural painkillers) are produced. If there is tissue damage anywhere, it can get cleaned up and repaired that much quicker. The immune function is better prepared to do its job and fight any enemy cells such as viruses, bacteria, and cancer.

Moving Fluids: Circulatory Effects

Concept 3: Fluid Balance

Every living cell in the body (and that's a really big number, even if you're a Chihuahua) needs fuel delivered to it and waste products taken away, more or less constantly. This delivery system is an important aspect of the body's metabolism, the ability of cells to process nutrients and waste products properly. Without this, the cells can't function properly. Transportation of nutrients and waste products is provided by fluids, but for now let's imagine using delivery trucks and garbage trucks. We'll focus here on the circulation of blood, but there are other fluids in the body, too, such as lymphatic fluid, which we'll look at when we consider the immune system, and also the fluid matrix in and between every cell in the body. We are, after all, about 60 percent water.

How does massage stimulate fluid circulation? And how does that help the body? One way was just mentioned in discussing stress and neurological effects. Remember that part of the relaxation response in the nervous system is to dilate blood vessels. This makes it easier for blood to move along its path. However, there may still be certain areas that have reduced or slowed blood flow due to restrictions, tight muscles, shallow breathing, scar tissue, adhesions, or inflammation. These areas could be as small as the tip of your little finger, as large as the whole body, or anywhere in between. Massage can dramatically improve the thoroughness and efficiency of circulation in these areas by relaxing muscles and mechanically unsticking adhesions and other restrictions. Many massage strokes also directly help move the fluids along their pathways, just like you can "massage" your toothpaste up and out of the top of the tube. (Well, at least a little bit like that.)

For the body as a whole, and on a daily basis, exercise is actually the best way to stimulate circulation. But exercise doesn't always happen for many reasons: injuries, confinement, boredom, arthritis, desk jobs (oops, we're supposed to be focusing on animals). And if we're talking about a specific tight or restricted area, then even exercise won't be enough to get *those* cells well taken care of. Massage, on the other hand, can be an effective and efficient solution.

> *Staying well hydrated is very important for the health, comfort, and function of all tissues in the body, including muscles.*

Balancing Tensions: Structural Effects

Concept 4: Tensegrity

A big *wow factor* that happens quite often with massage and bodywork is having a pain or tension in one location relieved by a release in an apparently unconnected body part. In fact, most chronic aches and pains are actually caused by a restriction or imbalance somewhere else in the body, not where the pain is being felt or the movement is being limited. A simplified but also classic example is someone who goes for massage for a sore or tight low back, gets massage in that area, goes home feeling better, and wakes up the next morning with the same low back problem. In this example it's not until she gets some release for the tight hamstrings (backs of the thighs) that she finally starts making some real progress for her back. Fortunately, there are common patterns that bodyworkers become familiar with, which can help them get more lasting results for their clients more efficiently. These are only general patterns, however. Each individual is unique and there are no cookie-cutter recipes that work for everyone.

The concept that explains how the above wow factor works is known as *tensegrity*. Imagine trying to build a house with only rubber bands. (Okay, let's say it's a very small house.) It would never hold a shape, would it? Too flexible, and with no integrity or strength. If you build a house with only strong, rigid parts, though, it may hold its shape nicely for a while, but what if something heavy falls on it or it gets shaken up in an earthquake? It will break because it has no flexibility, no resilience. A tensegrity structure, on the other hand, has a combination of elastic parts (providing tension) and rigid parts (providing integrity) that holds its original shape with a perfect balance of tensions. If something smashes this type of structure down, rather than breaking it simply gets a distorted shape as the tensions are redistributed. When the pressure is released, it pops back to its original shape.

Let's compare this idea to a living body. Many of us likely grew up (so far) thinking that our bones support the rest of our body like bricks in a brick building, one stacked on top of the other, supporting the next one above it, and so on. *Wrong!* Our bodies are tensegrity systems. Our bones are the rigid spacers and our system of muscles and connective tissue, or *fascia*, provides the elastic tension. This is an important distinction when comparing the results of being stressed. If a brick building has one corner smashed that corner is pretty much toast, while the rest of the building may be totally unaffected. This is not how our bodies work. If one part of the body is injured, the whole body is going to experience some effect, whether we notice it or not. The good news, though, is that the whole body can also experience *positive* effect when one part is rebalanced, just as the whole tensegrity structure regains its shape and rebalances tensions when the pressure that was distorting it is released.

When bodywork focuses on this tensegrity quality of our bodies, you can get significant and lasting changes in the alignment of the whole musculo-skeletal system (all the muscles and bones). This results in more efficient posture and movement, which in turn reduces stress, tension, and damage to muscles, joints, and everything else. And by the way, it's not only muscles and bones that are physically linked in this tensegrity system, but also organs, nerves, membranes, blood vessels, the brain, everything! When you hear bodyworkers using terms like fascial work, Structural Integration, Myofascial Release (MFR), or Craniosacral Therapy, among others, they are focusing, at least in part, on skeletal alignment through this tensegrity concept.

By the way, *fascia* with an *sc* is pronounced *fa-shuh* (like *fa-scinating*). or *fah-shuh*, but not *fay-shuh*, which would be spelled *facia*, a different word. You can go to a spa and get a facial, but that's not about fascia!

Efficient Movement: Habits and Patterns

Concept 5: Proprioception *(pro-prio-cep-tion)*

We and our animals all have habitual ways we stand, sit, and move our bodies. Some of these patterns may be efficient and highly functional, but for most of us, including our animals, they are not all so optimal. Good quality physical training that develops strength, flexibility, and balance can improve these habits and patterns dramatically. There are also many forms and aspects of bodywork that focus on the issue of body awareness and movement re-education. Animals, even more so than people, depend on such help from a bodyworker, therapist, or trainer to improve their posture and dysfunctional patterns of movement.

How do changes in movement patterns occur, for better or worse? Proprioception. There are specialized cells throughout the body called proprioceptors, primarily in and around joints. These cells send signals to the brain about position in and movement through space. Proprioception is the key difference between a well-conditioned klutz and a talented, agile athlete. The better the proprioception, the better the communication between the brain and the body. But when the brain learns, whether by habit or as a response to injury, that the movement available at a joint is less than perfect, it will continue to move only within that range until any problem (swelling, pain, adhesion, etc.) is resolved, and also until the proprioceptors and the brain are retrained to recognize the full potential again, the full range of motion.

A classic example is someone walking with a limp even after a broken bone has healed and the cast has been removed. But poor or dysfunctional proprioception can also happen without injury, simply by lack of movement or due to emotional patterns expressed in posture, for example. If the body doesn't use each joint in all ranges of motion for which it was designed, at least once in a while, then over time the system will forget what was actually the true normal, the full potential, and settle for whatever is used in the habitual movements. Quality training, bodywork, and stretching can all effectively give positive input to the proprioceptor cells in and around the joints, improving proprioception and efficiency of movement and posture.

Promoting Health: Immune Function

Concept 6: The Lymphatic System

How does the immune system work to protect the body against disease, and how does massage support it? All physical systems of our bodies (circulatory, lymphatic, neurological, digestive, respiratory, etc.) actually contribute to immune function. Elements such as physical barriers (skin and connective tissue), good bacteria (on the skin and in the digestive system), pH balancing, temperature regulation, special cells that fight germs, transportation of fighter cells and waste products through lymph vessels, lymph nodes that filter and cleanse the lymph fluid—all of these and more play a part in the body's ability to resist and recover from illness.

What role does massage play? For one thing, look back at concept 2. The immune system is supported and stimulated when the rest and relaxation mode is dominant. Circulation (concept 3) is another key; for the blood, yes, but also for the circulation of the lymphatic system, which is what we'll focus on now. This system operates much like the system of veins for blood, including the fact that exercise and massage are two of the best ways to stimulate it. The main difference is that rather than transporting blood cells and plasma, it's transporting lymph fluid. Lymph, like the blood, acts as both delivery trucks and garbage trucks for all cells in the body. But the deliveries are more focused on situations needing repair (injuries and infections), and the garbage trucks are focused on slightly different items, maybe we could say more of the actual garbage versus the recycling bins.

Virtually any massage will have positive effects for immune function, though it is also possible to experience (temporarily) some flu-like symptoms following a massage. This is usually because there have been lots of waste products piling up (garbage trucks on strike?), and when you draw the body's attention to it and finally tackle the now much bigger job, it is bound to be uncomfortable for a while. Would you rather continue in denial and let the garbage keep piling up? I hope not!

Lymphatic massage (also known as Lymphatic Facilitation or Manual Lymphatic Drainage) focuses on moving fluids along this delicate lymphatic system. It is often used with great success to reduce edema (swelling), and it also supports the general immune function of the body.

These six concepts should give you plenty to think about, for your animals and for yourself. There is just so much going on in the body, and so many ways that massage can support it: in muscle comfort, strength, and flexibility; in relaxation and reduced stress; in circulation and metabolism; in efficient alignment, posture, and movement; and in healthy immune function. I encourage you to return to this chapter and read about the concepts again, one at a time, as you massage your horse using the techniques you will learn in chapter 7. Remember, too, that you can find many resources to deepen your understanding of these physiological processes and anatomy, as well as other massage topics, by going to *www.AllAboutAnimalMassage.com* and asking questions, reading articles, newsletters, and books, and interacting with others through the "Animal Wellness Network."

4

Adaptation Versus Healing

After having read the previous chapters, it may seem miraculous to you that any of our animals, or us for that matter, have ever survived without regular massage. While this *is* an admirable feat (you can ask any massage therapist), the evidence suggests that it is indeed possible, and there are two main reasons for this. One is movement. Move it or lose it, so they say. (Fortunately, exercise is hugely beneficial to our health. Unfortunately, we don't tend to move quite as much as our ancestors did, nor do most of our animals.) Another reason is that so often our survival is managed more by *adaptation* to an injury or other problem than by fully healing from it.

Fortunately, Unfortunately

In fact, the process of recovery from an injury all too often can be described as a continuous cycle of "fortunately, unfortunately, fortunately, unfortunately . . ."

- Fortunately, our bodies have amazing powers to adapt and change as needed.

- Unfortunately, this process of adaptation can often create new challenges.

Picture a mildly traumatic injury, such as young horse falling while racing around a slippery corner. Say there is some bruising, and various ligaments and tissues are strained in the effort first to avoid and then to recover from the fall.

- Fortunately, the body sends various elements (delivered in blood and lymph) to clean up damaged tissue and make repairs.

- Unfortunately, these elements arrive in excess fluid (edema, or swelling), which increases pressure and pain in the area.

- Fortunately, this pain can help remind the body to move carefully while repairs are underway.

- Unfortunately, some of the fluid tends to hang around much longer than it needs to, partly due to the lack of movement already mentioned. It then becomes thicker and stickier, i.e. gluey, and adhesions and restrictions begin to develop.

- Fortunately, there now seems to be less suffering because the body is adapting to the restricted movement and pain, learning to recognize a new "normal" as proprioception adapts to the new situation.

- Unfortunately, now various structures (muscle, bone, tendon, ligament, blood vessels, nerves, you name it) are, in fact, glued together (adhesions), and range of motion (movement) is physically restricted.

- Fortunately, the body has many other parts, near and far, which can make up for this compromised and restricted area's shortcomings. This is known as compensation.

- Unfortunately, this eventually leads to the same cycle of stress and strain for those parts doing the compensating, because they are now having to work overtime.

This scenario works much the same for repetitive stress type injuries as it does for more traumatic ones like the fall in this example. Of course, the power of our bodies to adapt in these ways really *is* quite amazing and highly useful, just also less than perfect. *Fortunately*, what the body can do, it can generally undo, with a little help. Interventions like massage and other therapies can transform the scenario above to one where restrictions are released or even prevented in the first place, full range of motion is restored, and compensation patterns are no longer needed as the whole system returns to its original balance.

Injuries: A Team Approach

An injured animal will ideally have a team of care providers. You, your veterinarian, the trainer if you have one, and your massage professional are key members of the team. Massage can be a practical and compassionate way to help your horse when he has been injured. It's important to remember that during recovery from an injury, surgery, or other trauma, an animal's massage needs are going to be different from the normal routine. An injured horse's veterinarian should be consulted and give consent before beginning a program of therapeutic massage.

In the early stages of healing, specific techniques such as Manual Lymphatic Drainage can help decrease swelling and support the immune system. Further into the healing process, scar tissue can be effectively worked with to prevent adhesions and promote functional arrangement of the fibers, helping the scar tissue itself develop with optimal strength and flexibility. And further along still, appropriate stretches and other techniques can help range of motion and body awareness return more completely and positively.

Throughout the entire recovery period, massage can also be used to support the rest of the body, working to alleviate patterns of stress and compensation, including those patterns that may have contributed to the injury in the first place. Massage can be very helpful to relieve boredom and depression during recovery from an injury or illness. Heightened feelings of well-being greatly enhance the healing process.

When an animal is recovering from an injury, the advanced training and expertise of a massage professional can support you in many ways. The therapist will want to see the animal at certain intervals, which will vary depending on the trauma, the other treatments received (including those provided by you), the goals for recovery, and resources (time, finances, experience).

In between the professional sessions, there is much that you can do to support the healing process and the work begun by the bodyworker. During rehabilitation, daily attention, even multiple times a day, can be extremely helpful. Be sure to use the professional as a teacher to show you what's most appropriate and beneficial for your horse's needs. She can make decisions about prioritizing goals; about which techniques to use, when, and how often; about which directions to work, how much pressure to use, and so on. In any therapeutic situation, you and your massage professional have the same goal—your horse's health and well-being—and she will be happy to work with you and your veterinarian in a team approach.

> *The body is a healing machine. It wants to be balanced and is capable of rebalancing itself (potentially, if also imperfectly). Any modality that helps the body be more connected within itself, and on multiple levels, will help it function closer and closer to its potential.*

Your horse's body and your learning can both benefit from an appointment with a professional.

5

Finding and Working with
a Massage Professional

Part two of this book will give you many massage techniques you can use for your horse. Let's say you've been massaging your horse on your own. When and why would you decide to call in a professional? Here are some scenarios where a professional bodyworker or massage therapist can help you and your horse.

- You're noticing a pattern of tension, pain, or restricted range of motion with which you'd like to make better progress.

- You'd like a professional's assessment of your horse's tension patterns that your level of skill and experience may not detect.

- Your horse sustains an injury and needs the more advanced skills of a professional.

- You and your horse have a competition or other event coming up, and you want your horse to have every possible advantage.

- You want to observe and learn more from what a professional bodyworker can show you in person.

- You love the idea of regular massage for your horse, but just don't have time to do it yourself.

It is very important to understand that massage and bodywork professionals are neither trained nor licensed to provide any diagnosis, prognosis, or medical treatment of any kind. Always call your veterinarian first if there is even a suspicion that there is a current medical situation such as an injury or illness. If your veterinarian approves, the therapist can provide appropriate, supportive complementary attention, such as massaging areas of the body that are working to compensate for an injury, or promoting relaxation, circulation, healing, and many other benefits.

How do you go about finding a professional and scheduling an appointment? What should you ask? What should you expect from him, and what might he expect from you? Does your state regulate animal massage, and if so, what qualifications are required?

To find a massage therapist or bodyworker for your horse, start by asking other professionals such as your trainer, veterinarian, or farrier if they have recommendations. Of course, another excellent approach is asking friends and acquaintances who they've worked with and if they've experienced positive results. You can expand your list of options further with resources on the Internet, including my website, *www.AllAboutAnimalMassage.com*, where you can do a search within our "Animal Wellness Network" for animal care professionals near you, including massage therapists and bodyworkers. Tack and feed stores often have bulletin boards with business cards and fliers from local professionals, as well. And of course, you can find advertisements in horse-related publications and at events like shows and expos.

You and Your Professional: Working Together

Before, during, and after your appointment, there are specific things you can ask and do to optimize the experience for you and your horse, and to assist the professional in doing the best job for you. Your observation skills during the first appointment, the following days, and over the next few appointments will help you learn more about the therapist's work and your horse's body and responses.

Questions to ask before making an appointment

Q: *Can you tell me about your experience, training, certification, licensing, background, specialty, approach, etc? (Choose one or two or more words that work for you. You can also ask for references from among his clients.)*

A: Many answers could be fine, depending on your animal's needs, your goals, and any regulations existing in the state you live in (see "Regulations," page 30). As a point of reference, most certification programs for animal massage are between 50 and several hundred hours. Most licensing or certification programs for human massage are 500 to 1000 hours. You can get some sense of where the therapist falls within these ranges, though remember that continuing education hours (training taken after initial certification or licensing) are also significant. Of course, experience is also important but typically harder to measure or compare, so just listen and get your own sense as best you can.

Q: *What are your rates, and how long is a typical session?*

A: A useful comparison is the rates in your area for massage or bodywork for people. Although that's generally going to cover a wide range, you can get a sense of the average.

Q: *Do I need to be there for the appointment?*

A: Of course it's best that someone who knows the horse be there at least for the first appointment. Some therapists may require the owner to be present at the first or all appointments, which could relate to their philosophy, modality (type of bodywork), horse-handling skills, past experiences, or any combination of these or other factors. Many professionals will work without the owner there once they know the horse, which is an obvious benefit to scheduling ease.

Q: *Do you prefer to work before or after my horse is exercised, fed, etc?*

A: This will be partly dependent on the information you provide about your horse's routines, energy level, issues, distractions, and what the goals are for the session. It is ideal to find a time of day that the distractions will be minimal, so your horse can best focus on and receive the bodywork.

Q: *If another event is also on your horse's calendar, such as a show, long trail ride, chiropractic appointment, or other veterinary appointment: Is it best to schedule the bodywork for before or after the appointment or event? How soon before or after?*

A: You may need to coordinate some communication between the massage professional and your trainer, veterinarian, or anyone else involved. What are the goals for the bodywork session? Is it to prepare your horse for an upcoming event or help her to recover from it, or both? Has the horse received bodywork before? If she has, her responses will be more predictable than if she hasn't. This may affect decisions about timing, since the changes produced by massage may take the horse and/or the rider a day or two to adjust to. Regarding chiropractic care, my experience is that massage either before or after can be just fine, with different advantages to each. Whichever work comes first, the next professional's work is supported by the progress already made. If the horse is lame or in apparent pain, you should first call the veterinarian, who may also be the chiropractor. In each individual case, it will be best simply to ask any professionals involved, beginning with your veterinarian, about what their preferences and advice are.

Q: *What is your cancellation policy?*

A: Many will have one, some may not. The more notice you can give, the more helpful it is. Of course, it's also helpful for each of you to have a phone number to call for updates and last minute changes.

Being prepared for the appointment

- Have your horse reasonably clean and dry. Otherwise, expect that the therapist will either charge extra for grooming (using your own brushes only), or he'll use part of the session time for it, according to his preference or policy.

- Have a place available with shelter from rain, wind, mud, and sun.

- Allow the therapist some flexibility in timing, or make it clear when scheduling if you can't. Though you should expect him to respect your time, driving from place to place can make timing a challenge for the therapist.

- Be ready to give information relating to your horse's behavior, medical conditions, medications, past injuries, surgeries, etc.

During the appointment

- A great thing to do during the session is to focus on your own breathing. This will help your horse and will also help you stay tuned in to her responses and communication.

- Avoid petting, grooming, feeding, or excessive or loud talking during the massage. This can be distracting and potentially interfere with your horse's focus, communication with the therapist, and the results achieved. Of course sometimes your touch, handling, or reassurance may be helpful, so ask the therapist what he prefers.

- Watch what the therapist does, and ask questions about things you can do yourself between sessions.

- Observe how often your horse seems tuned in to her own body and how much she seems to participate in the process with the therapist versus either ignoring or resisting the work. Keep in mind that distractions in the environment can interfere with this, for some more than others. There is also a definite learning process to receiving bodywork. For some horses it takes about a minute to figure it out. For others it can take several sessions or more. For most it's somewhere in between.

- Signs of relaxation and release during the session (lowering head, soft eyes, yawning, deeper breathing, etc.) are positive. Even more important are the effects you'll notice over the next several days. Also look at cumulative changes over the course of several sessions.

- Don't judge the session by whether your horse falls asleep or is doing advanced yoga by the end, nor by whether the therapist looks like he's working hard, talks with a lot of technical terms, or charges a lot of money.

- Expect some ebb and flow between states of focus, relaxation, and even temporary agitation when an area is sore or compromised in some way. Does the therapist help your horse through these challenges in a positive manner? Is the area left alone because the horse doesn't like it? This option may be a great temporary solution for the sake of trust building or to get some releases happening elsewhere in the body, but an area of concern needs to be addressed or actively worked toward, unless it's beyond the skill or scope of the therapist.

At the end of the appointment

- Expect the professional to tell you his observations about your horse's areas of tension, indications of restrictions, tenderness, pain, or worry. He will also often tell you whether range of motion for various joints was normal or reduced, or triggered a pain response. He may watch your horse move and share observations about that and about general posture. Additional, specific observations and language may vary depending on the therapist and the type of bodywork being done.

- You should not expect or ask for a diagnosis of any kind. Nor can the therapist tell you specifically why your horse has certain tensions, restrictions, or discomforts. He *can*, however, teach you about how the body works and why certain types of causes can lead to certain types of effects.

- Each horse is completely individual and so will be the healing process. For this reason, the professional won't be able to tell you how long improvements will take or even whether massage will produce your desired results. He may be able to share some examples of what has happened for other clients in similar situations, though, which can give you a sense of what is possible.

After the massage

- Be sure your horse has water available, and also a chance to relieve herself. The changes that happen during bodywork often require a more than usual amount of the body's water for processing, resulting in thirst and a full bladder.

- If possible, give your horse a chance to move soon after the session to integrate the changes that happened during the massage. This helps her awareness and proprioception integrate the release of restrictions, increases in range of motion, and increases in comfort. The best form of movement for this process will depend on your horse's soundness and comfort, what changes happened during the session, and the skills of the person working with her. Options can include hand-walking, long lining, groundwork exercises, lunging, riding, or turnout.

- Using your own judgment, follow the bodyworker's recommendations about exercise, rest, or appointments. You are ultimately responsible for choosing which advice to follow for the sake of your horse and for yourself. If you choose not to follow the recommendations, however, you may or may not get the results you're looking for, or as quickly as you might hope.

- Observe your horse over the next few days and weeks. Does her movement, mood, or energy level change? How does she behave? How does she respond when you groom her? Does she hold her tail or head and neck differently? Stumble less? Have a change in appetite? Lie down to sleep more?

- Do feel free to call and talk with the professional as needed between sessions, whether to ask questions about your observations or the follow-up recommendations he may have made. He will also generally welcome hearing about your observations since the previous session.

- Does your horse have any stiffness the first day or two after the session? Stiffness can mean several different things. It could be due to excessive pressures used by the therapist, but it could just as easily be due to the natural healing process, release of toxins, rebalancing tensions, strengthening weaker muscles, and so forth. If you have any concerns about your horse's responses, be sure to call the therapist and/or your horse's veterinarian to discuss your observations.

- Give the therapist feedback, either at the next appointment or sooner, about your observations. Remember, you are a team.

Scheduling the next appointment

- Recommendations from the professional for the timing of the next session will vary depending on how your horse is doing, what the goals are, and in some cases the type of bodywork being done.

- For new clients, I find it helpful to schedule a second session fairly soon, say within one to three weeks, if there are some significant issues to be addressed. A longer interval is fine if the horse seems to be doing quite well. Of course, more often is always beneficial for prevention and maintenance, if you prefer that for your horse.

- By the end of the second session you will have much more information, including your observations during the interim since the first appointment. This will give you a better idea of how quickly your horse is responding to massage.

- Looking at your goals together, you and the therapist can both then better estimate the optimal frequency of sessions going forward. As time goes on, adjustments to the plan can be made as the situation develops.

Creating a working relationship with a professional bodyworker may take a little time. Use your own judgment, observation, and intuition when deciding whether to continue making appointments with the same person, try someone new, or do a combination of both. You may want to try more than one appointment before making a decision, though. Your horse may need some time to develop trust. There may be significant pain or imbalance issues that simply take more time to address. Remember that progress is not always obvious or measurable, and it's natural that some sessions will produce more obvious results than others. Countless factors contribute to the fact that each session is different. If you don't feel a clear sense of benefit after a few sessions, however, I would urge you to consider another person.

Take Care of Yourself for Your Horse's Sake

Your own personal familiarity with massage and other forms of bodywork can benefit your horse. The more you receive bodywork yourself, the more educated you will become as a receiver and consumer. This in turn will help you in making decisions about services for your animals. And if you are a rider, the bodywork you receive can help even more directly, since your own body has a significant impact on the horses you ride. It's remarkable how often body issues and tension patterns are mirrored between animal and owner, especially horses and riders, and addressing both together can provide even more progress than supporting only one of the partners.

Some therapists are licensed to work on both people and animals. In this case, you and your horse may have the opportunity to receive bodywork from the same person, which can give you very direct information about her work. Don't rule out the therapist who does not do people, however. Many excellent therapists prefer to devote themselves to helping our animal companions.

What's In a Name?

In most cases, the term a professional uses to describe herself will tell you very little about her qualifications. Here are just a few samples of labels you may come across, but know that you will still want to be asking questions about training and experience.

When it comes to animal massage, any of the labels listed below generally will be prefaced with Horse/Equine, Dog/Canine, Large Animal/Small Animal, Cat/Feline, etc. The title may also begin with Licensed or Certified. Licensed means that your state has some official means of licensing individuals for the profession, and that this individual has been through that process. Certified means she's taken a course that gave her a certificate at the end, but it doesn't tell you about what that course involved.

You will come across titles like Massage Therapist, Massage Practitioner, Bodyworker, Sports Massage Therapist, Acupressure or Shiatsu Practitioner, Structural Integration

Practitioner, Rolfer, etc. More terms exist, but these are some of the more common. Some terms are specifically trademarked by a particular school and can only be used by those graduates.

Interestingly, I've come across some objection to using the terms *therapist* or *practitioner* at all in referring to animal massage, even though these are the terms most often used by massage professionals for people. One suggestion (not my own) is that we use the term Massage Provider instead, also a perfectly useful title. Such distinction in terms is closely intertwined with the whole issue of whether animal massage constitutes practicing veterinary medicine, an on-going hot topic in many states.

Regulations

What follows is some much-abbreviated information on regulations related to animal massage, for your education and interest. You do not need to feel responsible for this information in seeking services for your animals. It is the provider's responsibility to understand any regulations applying to the work in her own state if she's in business and charging for services.

The legal question of animal massage is a still-evolving issue that varies from state to state, year to year, day to day, and also sometimes according to your information source. Many states do have regulations, and many more are in the process of determining them. Some states include massage in the definition of "veterinary medicine," and therefore do not allow it outside of veterinary practices. There is great debate about whether this approach, or any other form of regulation, is an appropriate solution. You may choose to ignore the issue, or gather information from people you know, including your veterinarian, or you may feel inclined to research it thoroughly online. You may even feel inclined to become involved with your own state's decisions about this aspect of animal care.

One resource that you may find helpful is the International Association of Animal Massage and Bodywork. You can find this association online via a link on *www.AllAboutAnimalMassage.com*, or through an Internet search engine. The IAAMB is a professional organization for animal massage therapists and bodyworkers, though membership is open to anyone who supports animal massage. Their website includes information on laws and regulations by state. The IAAMB chart on the topic is very handy and informative, though they can't be held responsible for guaranteeing that the information is always completely up-to-date. They do have updates on news from various states as issues come up. They also provide links and guidance to go directly to your own state's legislative website to research the current situation in your state.

Why, you may ask, doesn't this book include pictures and names of all the muscles? Well, at a beginning stage it really won't help you learn massage. The anatomy included with each technique in part two will give you a great start, however. When and if you are interested in learning more anatomy, please visit www.AllAboutAnimalMassage.com for resources.

Part Two

Massaging Your Horse

The more you learn about being safe and effective, the more fun you will have massaging your horse.

6

Guidelines for
Effectiveness and Safety

Before you begin massaging your horse, know that massage is not a substitute for proper veterinary care. Please do not delay in calling your veterinarian if your horse is in pain or showing any symptoms of injury or illness.

Contraindications and Precautions

For healthy animals, there is little worry about causing any harm with massage as long as you are using reasonable judgment about the pressures you use and always pay attention to your horse's feedback. If your horse has an illness, injury, or medical condition, certain types of massage and bodywork can still be very beneficial to aid the healing process. However, in these cases the effects of massage could also be harmful, depending on the specific condition, whether the symptoms are acute, and what techniques are used and how they are applied. Before massaging any animal with an illness, injury, or medical condition, be sure to consult with your veterinarian.

- Do not massage any animal who has a fever or systemic infection, or one who is in a state of shock.

- Do not massage directly over areas of current injury, local infection, or recent surgery.

- If you have any question about whether certain techniques or massage in general are appropriate for your animal's medical situation, please ask your veterinarian. This includes, but is not limited to, conditions involving the heart, kidneys, liver, and circulation.

It is possible that your horse could experience adverse reactions during or after a massage. This may depend on underlying conditions, past experiences, remnants of past medications or anesthesia in the body, or massage techniques being applied too intensely for that individual. Typically, any adverse reactions are temporary and a natural part of the healing process as the body releases stagnant waste products, toxins, emotions, and restrictions. Examples include muscle stiffness, a change in energy level, hives, and reduced coordination (i.e., clumsiness). If your horse received a massage from someone other than yourself, you should call that person to discuss your observations. If you have any concerns, or if the reactions persist more than one or two days, consult with your veterinarian.

Although a few safety and handling suggestions are included, the intent of this book is not to teach animal handling. It is assumed that you will be working with your own animal, that you are familiar with your animal, and that you already know how to handle him safely and effectively. If you have questions about this for your situation, please consult a professional to help you.

The techniques I've chosen for chapter 7 are moves I use regularly in my own practice. They will help you monitor, support, and learn about your horse's body as you massage. I find them to be highly effective and easy to teach and learn. However, like many of the simplest arts, their effectiveness and your skill with them can be developed over a lifetime. I invite you and encourage you to return to this book and to the resources you will find on *www.AllAboutAnimalMassage.com* as you continue to learn and practice. Not only will you add new tools to your "toolbox" this way, but you will also continue to refine and rediscover the ones you've already learned. And remember that receiving massage is one of the very best ways to learn about giving massage, with some pretty great additional benefits as a bonus!

Effectiveness

> *"Whether you think you can, or you think you can't,*
> *either way, you are right."* —Henry Ford

Steps

1. Know that you *can* massage your horse effectively.

2. Listen to what your horse tells you.

3. Listen to your intuition.

4. Visualize positive results.

5. Keep on learning.

6. Keep on massaging!

Of course, your most important teacher in this lifelong learning process will be your horse, through the honest feedback he gives you. Although humans can (but often don't) give detailed, verbal feedback, the nonverbal feedback from the horses you massage will be constant, accurate, and very helpful, if you pay attention and recognize the responses. It is important that you develop the habit of watching your horse's face and body language as much as possible as you massage. He will tell you when to speed up, slow down, lighten up, or go deeper. He will tell you where he's tight, whether he's also sore, just a little worried, or especially focused. He may even show you where you should massage next.

As you massage, you will gather information largely from your horse's responses, but also from what your hands feel as they palpate (feel) his body. With practice you will increase your ability to feel evidence of less healthy or restricted tissue with your hands. This sensitivity will continue to develop as long as you continue practicing, even over a lifetime. The areas of tension and restriction may feel a number of different ways depending on just what is going on and for how long. They may feel like dryness: not like the skin is wet or dry but as if you're massaging a dry sponge rather than a moist sponge, or slightly dry clay versus moist clay. You may also feel that the tissue feels hard, gluey, or sticky, or has an uneven texture. You might notice that two structures (such as skin and underlying muscle, or two neighboring muscles) move as one lump mass rather than having some glide between them. Or you may not notice the sensations in your hands at all, but your horse may show a pain response or simply look at you differently or hold his breath.

Being able to confidently interpret all that your horse is telling you or what you feel with your hands is sometimes another story, however. Below are some tips to get you started. For more information related to these tips and others, I recommend *Massaging My Horse: A Guided Journal*, available as an e-book at *www.AllAboutAnimalMassage.com*. This journal is an interactive workbook containing questions and charts to guide you and help you record your observations. It includes additional information on interpreting your horse's feedback, movement, and posture; on what you feel with your hands and intuition; and on the results of the techniques. Not only will the journal support your development in all of these skills, but you will also end up with a record of the patterns in your horse's body and the changes that occur over time.

Top 10 Tips for Observing Your Horse's Feedback and Patterns

1. There are many signs of a release happening or the positive effect of your touch. These include a lowering of the head and neck, sleepy or soft eyes, licking and chewing, a sigh, deeper breathing, yawning, and releasing gas. (Any release is a good release, so I've heard!)

2. Signs of discomfort, pain, or ticklishness, or the anticipation of any of these, are all significant and may be improved (decreased) with bodywork. These include

raising of the head and neck, tail swishing, pawing, stomping, moving away, moving rudely or excessively into you, biting, kicking, tight lips, ears flat back, holding the breath, tensing muscles, or simply a worried look in the eye.

3. Some horses will give more subtle feedback than others, based on their experiences, training, and personality, as well as on how sore they are. You can also expect, over time, that your horse will learn to give more subtle, polite, and accurate feedback if you are paying attention and responding to it. That is, if he learns through experience that you are generally listening and responsive, he will stop "shouting" at you in his efforts to communicate.

4. Remember to be observant of the whole environment. Not every bit of body language or expression is feedback about the massage. Sometimes the horse may have an itch, get bothered by a fly, need to pee, get worried about a noise or smell, or make faces at another horse walking by. Check and see if you get some consistency in the reaction as you repeat what seemed to trigger it.

5. Compare left and right sides of the body in checking for reactions, heat or coldness, swelling, tension, mobility of joints or tissues, or textures such as the following: dry, gluey, sticky, thickened, hard, spongy, bumpy, squishy, zingy, along with the other descriptions you will create as you find them. When comparing tensions between right and left, be aware that how squarely the horse is standing can affect this feel. Other findings, though, such as the horse's responses or the textures of tissue, heat, etc., will not depend on whether he's standing evenly on all four feet.

6. Always thank your horse (out loud or silently) when he gives you some feedback. Even negative feedback is useful, as long as your safety is not compromised.

7. If your horse gives negative feedback signals (such as listed in number 2), you will need to find a balance between respecting his communication and being persistent in order to help him. While there are times to use some restraint for your safety (a handler, safe tying, or your hand on the halter), you must never *inflict* the massage on your horse. It is always possible to find some compromise, in time if not right away. You have many options. You can leave the area for now but don't forget about it. You can persist but with a variation of pressure, speed, or technique. Perhaps all you need to change is your own breathing, and relax. You can also enlist the help of a professional to work with your horse and to coach you.

8. Don't assume that the goal is to put your horse to sleep, though certainly relaxation is a positive sign. It is quite natural for your horse to go through waves of relaxation, alternating with higher energy and a desire to move. How much of each can depend on the application of the massage, but also on your horse's age, energy level, attention span, experience with bodywork, the time of day, and countless distractions and expectations, not to mention the degree of soreness.

9. Each observation you make is just one piece of information. Pay attention to it, remember it, even go ahead and assume it's significant, but also know that it may not mean exactly what it seems at first. The more observations you make that point toward the same conclusion, the more confidently you can make that interpretation.

10. Always pay attention to your intuition. There are more ways to receive information than just observation of body language or through palpation (touch).

Safety

The three aspects of safety that apply most directly to this book are restraint, stools, and your own body mechanics.

Restraint

What follows are some pointers on various options, starting from the most to the least amount of restraint.

1. **Tying or Cross-ties**

   Always make sure the horse has had appropriate and thorough training *before* tying.

   Always make sure the tie has a quick release knot, snap, material, or gadget (such as a Blocker Tie, available through the website).

   Make sure your horse has nonslip footing.

   Know that if she pulls back hard, she can easily injure her neck, even if the tie does not break. If the tie does break or she falls over, she may hurt a lot more than her neck, not to mention you or others nearby.

   Advantages: The horse may focus better into her own body and what you are doing. You can more safely use a stool (see below). It can be safer for the person.

   Disadvantages: Certain safety risks as mentioned above. The horse can't move freely or have access to water or "facilities" (she won't want to pee on a hard surface).

2. **Using a Handler**

   If using a handler, communicate clearly with him about how much freedom to allow the horse's head and body during various techniques. When working back from the base of the neck, have the handler on the same side as you. This way if the horse moves and circles around the handler, the hindquarters will swing away from you rather than toward you. When working on the head or forward part of the neck, the handler can either stand back or be on the other side to be out of your way. (Note: In the photographs illustrating the techniques in this book, as well as on the website, the handler is almost always on the opposite side from the therapist for the sake of full visibility for the photos.)

Advantages: Can be the best balance of safety, restraint, and freedom.

Disadvantages: The handler may be a distraction to the horse, even if doing everything right (not petting, feeding, talking excessively or loudly, etc.).

3. **Loose with Halter and Rope On**

I generally recommend having the halter on and rope attached (to the halter, not to you!), even if working with the horse loose (generally in a stall or other confined area). You can't always know when or how the horse will react to something unexpected, either in the environment or from the massage. It can greatly increase your safety, and possibly the horse's safety, if you are able to quickly (without startling the horse) hold the rope and maintain control. On the other hand, the rope can become a hazard in itself if you are not vigilant about where it is at all times. Make sure the horse can't step on it or get it caught on anything. Best options of where to place the rope are either draped over the horse's back or withers, draped over your arm (never wrapped), or actually held in one hand as you use the other to massage.

Advantages: Lots of freedom for the horse, no need for a handler, and without the possible risks of tying.

Disadvantages: You must focus as much on handling the horse and rope as on the massage. How much of a disadvantage this is depends on the horse's behaviors and on your horse-handling skills and comfort.

4. **Loose, No Rope**

This may be your first choice, and perhaps you already do much around and with your horse this way.

Advantages: No rope to keep track of or step on, and more importantly, simply a very different way of being with each other. You must use your own judgment to decide, knowing your horse and your own skills and experience, whether this is a good option for you.

Disadvantages: A safety risk with unexpected movements or behaviors.

Stools

Standing on a stool while massaging can increase risk of injury for both of you if your horse becomes frightened or simply moves unexpectedly or rudely. On the other hand, it can be helpful to your shoulders, wrists, and hands at times. All techniques in chapter 7 are taught without the need for a stool, assuming you are able to groom your horse without one. I've also included tips on body mechanics that protect your joints and muscles without resorting to the use of a stool.

If you do need or prefer to use a stool, please keep in mind the following suggestions.

1. Introduce your horse to the stool and the noises it can make before you stand on it next to her.

2. Only use a short stool that you can step off quickly without (as much) risk of falling in the process.

3. Use a stool with solid sides so there's no chance of your horse putting a foot through it.

4. Only use a stool on even, level ground, and with your horse either safely tied or held by a handler.

5. Something like a bale of hay can make a great stool, though then you must always position your horse to the stool rather than being able to move it to or around your horse.

Appropriate use of stool and handler, though the handler should be on same side as the person massaging for greater safety. Here she is on the opposite side for the sake of visibility in the photograph.

Body Mechanics

Look for examples of the following guidelines in the photographs in chapter 7. As much as possible:

1. Keep your back comfortably straight and upright.

2. Keep your wrists, fingers, and thumbs well aligned (straight), especially anytime you are using them to apply pressure. For the thumb this means in line with your forearm rather than straight out to the side.

3. Minimize use of thumbs and fingertips, saving them for when you really want them. When you do use them, use them together to support each other like splints rather than spread out too much.

4. Keep your knees soft and your feet under your center of gravity.

5. Keep your elbows near your sides when possible, or even braced against a hip, to reduce effort for your arms and shoulders.

6. If you need to reach low, either squat (keeping your back upright) or, if leaning over, rest one or both elbows on a thigh for support.

7. If you need to reach high, use both hands together to support each other and to support your shoulders.

8. Keep your shoulders relaxed and down, even when reaching high.

9. Have your movements come from your center and your feet and legs, rather than from your waist, back, and arms. (This one can be hard to see in photographs, so please check out the videos on the website *www.AllAboutAnimalMassage.com*.)

10. Breathe! This will help your body in every way, including oxygen supply and keeping your joints and muscles from stiffening.

Therapeutic Petting and Grooming

Try these three simple steps to add a therapeutic element to your everyday petting and grooming routines, as well as whenever you practice massage. By using the special techniques of breathing, listening, and visualizing, you will enhance communication with your horse and increase your ability to use therapeutic touch.

1. **Breathe.** It is amazing how powerfully therapeutic something as simple as the breath can be. Use your breath both to connect more completely with your horse and also to encourage her to breathe more regularly and deeply. People and animals alike hold the breath for any number of reasons: pain, worry, fear, stress, and also simply out of habit. When we shift to regular, deep, easy breathing (in and out the nose as much as possible), it relaxes and balances our nervous system and the health of our tissues.

    It is easy to forget and start holding your breath again when you are concentrating on something, like massaging your horse, for example. So give yourself frequent reminders. You might even make a sign or other visual reminder for yourself. You can also time your breath with the hand or brush strokes. This works quite beautifully. The more you practice, the more naturally the breath will flow, enhancing any massage you do. And you will benefit as much from the process as your horse.

    A great exercise for learning to breathe while you massage is to try the opposite, purposely hold your breath while massaging. (Well, just hold some breaths, and the rest of the time shallow breathing. You still need to stay conscious!) This way you can directly experience just how much better it feels, and how much better your horse will respond, when you do *breathe*!

2. **Listen.** In this special kind of listening you will primarily be using your hands, eyes, intuition, and heart. You can, of course, also use your ears to include any sounds your horse makes. Constantly observe, and let your horse know that you are observing by responding to her feedback. Does she turn to look at you or a

part of her body? Does she hold her breath? Does she move into or away from something? Notice if her eye is soft (relaxed, happy) or hard (worried, tense).

A massage is not something you do *to* your animal, but rather a constant conversation between her body and your hands. If you expect her to participate with you, you must always be listening to her part of the conversation. The more you practice together, the more your horse will tell you about what's going on in her body and mind.

Listen when your animal shows tension or worry, and respond with a change, such as lightening up, slowing down, or changing the type of stroke.

Then notice when a positive change occurs.

3.   **Visualize.** Picture the goal. Focus on what you want, rather than what you don't want. If your horse is holding her breath, for example, or showing tension in some other way, keep visualizing her breath deepening and her body relaxing, rather than focusing on tension. You can also visualize what's happening under the skin, such as blood flow increasing, adhesions melting, or nerves calming. Your ability to visualize will deepen with practice. The more you experience the changes you visualize, feeling them under your hands or observing them in your horse's body language, the more clearly and vividly you can picture them happening beforehand, and the more powerful your visualizations become.

Top Three Resources for Learning More Massage Skills

1. The ultimate resource: your horse! He or she can teach you (almost) everything you want to know.

2. Visit *www.AllAboutAnimalMassage.com*, where you can find classes and schools, video clips, articles, DVDs, books, tools, professional services, other websites and organizations, the "All About Animal Massage" newsletter, and more. You can also visit and join our "Animal Wellness Network," which connects you with other people around topics of caring for our animals, including massage and bodywork. A treasure trove of information to assist you in your learning adventure.

3. Have a professional massage your horse. Watch what he does; observe your horse's responses. Ask the professional to teach and advise you on your own horse's body.

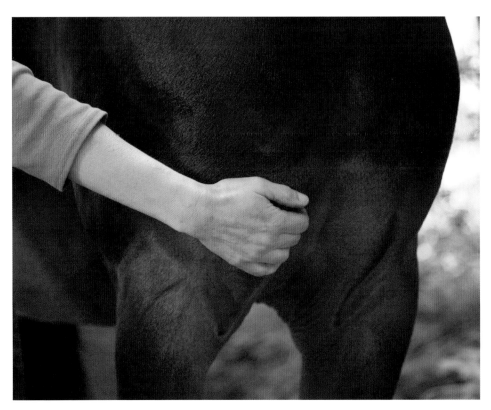

With even just a few basic techniques, you can create a variety of full body sessions to suit your horse's needs each time you massage.

7

Nine Basic Techniques
with Anatomy Connections

General Directions
Building Your Skills and Creating Sessions

Choose one or two new techniques to focus on learning during each session that you share with your horse. This will help keep the experience even more positive for both of you. Each session you do (after the first), begin by reviewing some of the techniques you've already practiced, and then add the new one or two for the day. I've arranged them in a sequence that works well to build on, eventually putting them together to create a basic, full-body massage. You don't have to go in this order, however. By following the guidelines below for creating a session, combined with reading your horse's feedback as discussed in chapter 6, you will learn to tailor each massage to your horse's own needs for that day.

When you're familiar with all nine techniques here, as well as some of the variations suggested, you will find many more techniques to learn from the following resources. *More Massage Moves for Horse Lovers* is an e-book available at *www.AllAboutAnimalMassage.com.* It contains additional Techniques, Anatomy Connections, and Coaching Tips to help you continue to build on all you learn here.

Most of the information in *More Massage Moves* is adapted from *The Dog Lover's Guide to Massage,* so if you are a dog lover, you may choose to purchase the book, adapting the techniques to your horse yourself.

You can also find more to learn in the free "All About Animal Massage" newsletter, and the articles, books, DVDs, and other resources available at *www.AllAboutAnimalMassage.com.*

Creating a Session

Choose a time of day and a location such that you and your horse can both focus, relax, and enjoy the process. Although eating can be a distraction to your horse, it can also be a relaxing time to massage. If your horse is eating, don't expect to receive the same level of participation and feedback; yet you don't need to rule out mealtime as a good time for massage.

It is important that there be some form of a beginning and an end to each session, a touch version of "Hello, would you like a massage?" and "Thank you, time to end now." Full Body Stroking (Technique 1) makes an excellent opening and closing for any massage. There are other options, too, such as a quiet touch on the back, chest, or head, and simply breathing some easy breaths together. Do always begin by asking your horse's permission and end with a thank you.

When transitioning from one technique to another, or one area of the body to another, use long strokes (as with Full Body Stroking) to connect your work. For example, if you just finished a technique for the neck and next you want to do a shoulder technique, use long strokes from where you just had your hands on the neck to connect into the shoulder before starting the next technique there. This will be much more pleasing to your horse and will also give him a clearer sensation of how the different areas of his body connect to each other and to his brain and awareness.

Always (when it works) have both hands touching your horse. Sometimes both hands will be active for the technique, but even when one hand is not active, it is still involved and connected for a supportive and grounding effect.

Choose one or two Coaching Tips to particularly focus on as you practice. For example, for Full Body Stroking you might choose using soft hands and visualizing blood flow. You can mix and match Coaching Tips with other techniques in many cases.

Variations: You can also mix and match techniques with different areas of the body. For example, try Strumming and Smoothing on the muscles of the forearm, or try Deep Strokes on the back of your horse's thigh. The more you practice, the more you will use your creativity to discover new combinations.

Length of Sessions: Start with anywhere from five to fifteen minutes for your first sessions, and build from there. Some horses will soak it up 24/7 (not really, but it seems like it), and some can only handle small doses for a while. Most are somewhere in between, with 45 to 75 minutes being a typical range for a professional massage.

Frequency of Sessions: This will depend on your horse's health and preferences, on the length of your sessions, the techniques you use, on your stage of learning, and just maybe on your schedule! For these techniques, every day could be fine for many horses, even multiple times a day, but you'll have to let your horse tell you for sure. For the learning process I would suggest at least once a week to maintain and build on your progress.

After a massage, hand-walk your horse for at least five or ten minutes so he moves his body and has a chance to feel and integrate the changes that happened. Doing stretches with your horse can also be helpful for this process of integration. You will find resources on learning stretch exercises at *www.AllAboutAnimalMassage.com*.

Note: Please read all of chapter 6, "Guidelines for Effectiveness and Safety," before practicing any of the following techniques on your horse.

Before practicing each new technique, read the full description along with its Coaching Tips and Anatomy Connection. Trying them out on yourself or a human friend is also a great way to get more feedback on your touch.

Technique 1
Full Body Stroking

Known technically as effleurage (pronounced ***eff-lur-ahge***), this stroke might seem too simple to count as massage, but if you practice with the three coaching tips below, you and your horse will both experience how therapeutic it is. Think especially about the circulatory effects you read about in chapter 3. In addition to being quite relaxing, effleurage is excellent for stimulating circulation. Understanding and visualizing this information clearly will enhance the effects.

You can begin on your horse's face or poll if that's a relaxing experience for him, or begin further back and return to the head later. Most often you will use full hand contact, but at times maybe you'll use fingers only, the back of your hand, or a forearm; whatever is most comfortable. Use long, rhythmic strokes that connect one region of the body into another. This will enhance your horse's sense of connection and wholeness in his body.

Swelling: Effleurage strokes are often applied in the same direction the coat grows for animals. Against the hair is also fine, as long as your horse does not object. If your horse has any swelling anywhere, you can encourage the excess fluids to return toward the heart, whether this direction is with or against the hair growth.

Notice that the stroke is connecting from the neck onto the shoulder rather than stopping at the base of the neck. The handler is nicely focused and present without being distracting. Normally the handler should be on same side as the person massaging, but is opposite here for the sake of the photo.

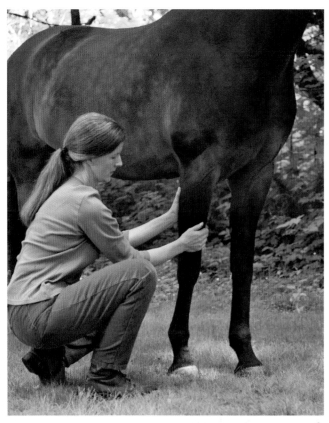

Remember to include the legs, all the way to the hoof.

Use long strokes to connect through the back and into the hindquarters. In large areas like this, the forearm can also join in the stroke. Notice the fingers connecting over to the other (right) side of the body, so the horse feels a connection right and left, though the focus of the stroke is on her left side.

Coaching Tips

1. **Breathe.** Quietly in and out through your nose. Feel your belly and ribs move gently with your breath. This will help your horse breathe, too.

2. Keep your hands soft, your shoulders relaxed, and your knees soft, not locked. This will all help your horse relax, as well. It will also help you to breathe.

3. **Visualize.** Many options here, so feel free to be creative. You can picture the blood flow being stimulated as the vessels relax and dilate (enlarge). You can picture a color or glow spreading slowly across your horse's body, as if you are carefully and thoroughly painting him with your hands. Visualize your horse running and playing with ease, comfort, and joy. Your visualization can really be anything, as long as it has these two qualities: it must be positive and it must be about your horse.

Anatomy: The Fascial Web

Effleurage and circulation make a great pair for using the powers of visualization to enhance a massage technique, as discussed above. But since you have already received information on the circulatory system earlier in the book, I will introduce here another huge, important, and wonderful Anatomy Connection that applies equally to all techniques. (Can you tell it's a favorite topic of mine?) Just as the long strokes of effleurage help your horse feel the interconnectedness of his entire body, the following information will help you see how thoroughly connected the body really is, cell to cell, region to region, and tissue to tissue.

Fascia, or connective tissue, forms a three-dimensional web of connections throughout the body, changing its form for different jobs as needed by changing the proportions of the molecules that make it up. An analogy, much closer to reality than you might think, would be using flour, sugar, salt, and water (maybe add a few spices?) to make many different foods, depending on the exact recipe. Even bone, for example, is connective tissue with calcium and other minerals added. Layers of connective tissue, including membranes around and within muscles (myofascia), membranes around organs and bones, and the layer of superficial fascia between the skin and underlying muscle, are known collectively as fascia. Tendons and ligaments are actually this very same fascial tissue concentrated into denser forms in order to connect muscle to bone (tendon) and bone to bone (ligament).

It's important to realize that connective tissue is not being used like glue or tape to join separate pieces together, but that the various parts are actually different aspects of one single Whole. *One* spider web spun from *one* strand of silk, so to speak. Thus, every cell in the body has a physical link to every other cell in the body. They are not merely floating side by side in the fluid that is between them.

Though technically not identical terms, *connective tissue* and *fascia* are often used interchangeably. For further fascinating facts about fascia (all the *a*'s following *f*'s should sound the same as you say that), check out the resources at *www.AllAboutAnimalMassage.com*.

Technique 2
Jostling

Place one or both hands on the crest of your horse's neck. Gently rock the crest side to side, starting with very small, slow movements that grow bigger as the neck relaxes. You can repeat this process with your hand on the underside of the neck as well, which can get even more jiggly as the head lowers.

Jostling the crest side to side.

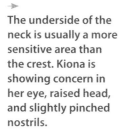

The underside of the neck is usually a more sensitive area than the crest. Kiona is showing concern in her eye, raised head, and slightly pinched nostrils.

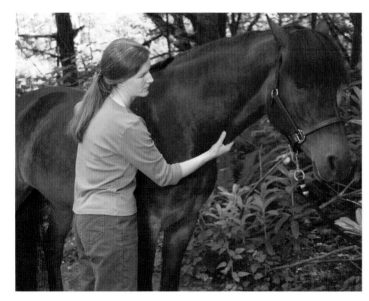

Starting to relax into it.

Coaching Tips

1. If your horse initially raises her head and neck, lighten your hand to zero pressure, keeping the contact if you can without creating more tension. Try again, making the movements even smaller and slower. Breathe. As your horse relaxes her neck, it will become easier to jostle.

2. Find a speed and size of jostle where the whole neck jiggles like Jell-O. Your hand is merely helping it keep its own rhythm with nudges in each direction.

Anatomy: The Parasympathetic Nervous System

As discussed in more detail in part one, the nervous system has two modes of being that we transition in and out of as needed for different situations. One is fight or flight, or in other words, stress! Very useful when appropriate for survival, but the rest of the time, not so helpful. The other mode is rest and relaxation. This latter is the parasympathetic system. Although each system can be stimulated by touch anywhere on the body, there are actually physical structures (nerves) in certain locations that relate to each system. And guess where many of the parasympathetic or rest and relaxation nerves are located: in the neck! So as you jostle the neck, you can think about not only the muscles, joints, and circulation that you're helping, but also that you are enhancing the body's parasympathetic responses, such as slower heart rate, decreased blood pressure, and stimulated digestion.

Technique 3
Deep Strokes

I'll include two in one here: compressions and glides. Each type of stroke will be applied with light pressure at first, only adding more pressure as the muscle relaxes and allows deeper work.

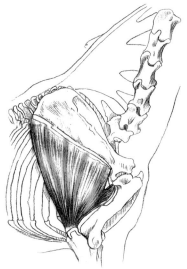

For the triceps muscle at the back of the shoulder, the compressions and glides can follow these lines.

Compressions: Start by practicing compressions along the back of the shoulder in the triceps muscle. Compressions are pumping movements that move fluids through the tissue; it's like squeezing out a dirty sponge repeatedly untill the water runs clean. Keeping your elbows near your side and your wrist straight, use the back of a relaxed fist and lean from your center as you compress into the muscle. Your other hand can support the working hand as seen in the photo. Ease back out of the compression and repeat, feeling for an easy rhythm. Start at the top of the muscle and make your way down to the elbow.

Glides: Next, using the same hand and body position, start again at the top of the triceps, but this time compress inward once and then slowly glide down to the elbow, following the same line as you did for the compressions. You will be following the direction of the muscle as you unstick adhesions and lengthen and realign tissue fibers.

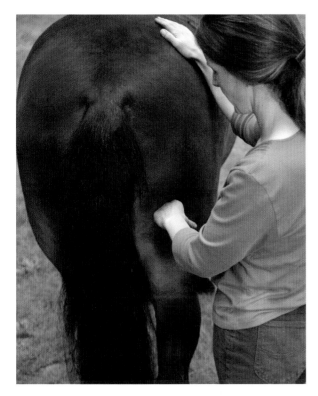

This same combination of compressions and gliding strokes works well at the back of the thigh, and really on almost any part of the body if you modify your body mechanics to suit the angle, height, size, etc.

Coaching Tips

1. "From your center" means thinking and feeling from your belly, pelvis, and even rooted down into your legs, instead of trying to use arm strength. Ideally you should feel like you could do this all day. Experiment with how you apply any stroke to find this feeling of working with ease from your center.

2. As a general guideline, the greater the pressure you use, the slower you go. Massaging too hard or too fast can create resistance from the horse or even the muscle tissue itself. Just as a horse will protect itself if it doesn't feel safe (and can't run away), muscles will protect themselves by guarding or tensing up. This resistance will feel like the muscle pushes back at you rather than letting you sink in. It will not help your horse to try to push through resistance. Lighten up, slow down, and breathe.

Anatomy: Triceps and the Stay Apparatus

Ever wonder how horses sleep standing up? Well, they have arrangements of muscles, tendons, and ligaments in their legs called the Stay Apparatus. In addition to this, the kneecap (patella) in the stifle joint of the hind leg can also get into a locked position, so virtually no muscle effort is needed to stay standing in the hind end. In the front legs, however, the triceps muscle must be a little bit activated to keep the elbow straight since it can't lock like the stifle does. This is why you will sometimes see elbows and knees starting to buckle as a horse is falling deeply asleep or is sedated. So, while they can do most of their sleeping standing up, they need to lie down for their deepest sleep. Horses who have trouble lying down and getting up unfortunately miss out on these deep sleeps, making it more challenging for their bodies to get the most thoroughly restorative and healing rest. Likewise, horses often experience extra stress in the triceps (along with the rest of the body) after a long trailer ride or during periods of stall rest. Stressed triceps muscles can also cause or be caused by stress in the muscles along the back of the forearm. Some of these muscles share the triceps' job of extending the elbow. As one muscle weakens from stress, another doing the same or a similar job must take up more of the load. And guess where the tendons of these forearm muscles run: down the back of the lower leg, where so many lameness problems can develop when the muscles above are fatigued.

Technique 4
Strumming and Smoothing

Another two in one technique, the words *strumming* and *smoothing* describe the feeling of working your fingers through the muscles in different directions. First you will be strumming across the fibers, feeling for any little "guitar strings" (tight bands of muscle) or knots (adhesions) that may be there. Even if you don't feel any, you will be helping to decrease any tension and tenderness, and preventing adhesions from developing. Next, smooth out the fibers, realigning and lengthening them as you apply each stroke. This is like the gliding deep stroke in technique 3, though here for the pectoral muscles of the chest you'll be using fingers and palm rather than the back of your fist.

Important Safety Tip: **Many horses are quite sensitive in the chest and grouchy about having it massaged. This, and any other area of soreness, ticklishness, or reactivity, including the girth and belly, is never "just the way they are," but rather a loud and clear request for help. You may need to have your horse either safely tied or use a handler to keep yourself safe from a bite or kick when massaging areas that are sore or sensitive. You must still be respectful of the horse's requests that you lighten up or slow down as needed to keep her reasonably comfortable with the process.**

Begin by standing at your horse's shoulder, watching her face and eyes as you stroke from the neck or shoulder into the chest area. Repeat a few effleurage strokes on the chest, and locate the sternum, or breastbone, in the middle of the chest.

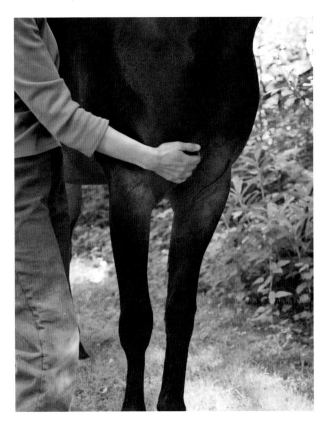

Hook your fingers gently into the muscle tissue at the edge of the sternum. Your fingers will be slightly curved, but with finger pads doing the hooking, not fingernails. Pull or curl your fingers toward you. Initially you may find tight cords of muscle bundles. Strum back and forth over them several times each as you come across them. Eventually, or maybe right away for some horses, you will find you can sift through with less interruption from these "speed bumps."

Next you will smooth out the same tissue, but now perpendicular to the direction you did the strumming, starting at the top of the chest and stroking toward the belly. You can also hook and pull your finger pads in the opposite direction, from between the forelegs toward the top of the chest. The muscles will get the same benefit of improving circulation, decreasing tension, and unsticking adhesions in either direction, so choose whichever works best for you and your horse.

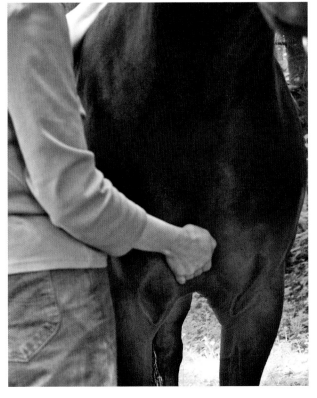

Coaching Tips

1. If you find your horse is not ready for the strumming and smoothing, try gently slapping the chest muscles instead, which can actually be easier for many to accept and relax into. If you consistently find your horse very reactive, take advantage of professional services to help your progress.

2. Release the strokes as slowly and thoughtfully as you apply them. The release is as much a part of the technique as the application.

Anatomy: The Pectoral Sling

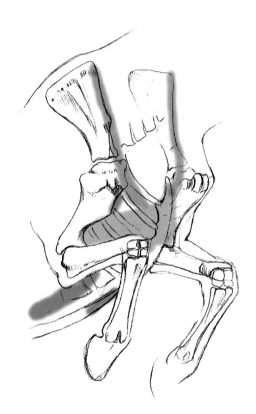

There are actually four pectoral muscles that form a group. Here the "scapular pec" is shown in gold, the descending and transverse pectorals are shown in green, and the ascending pectoral is shown in blue.

The pectorals are part of a sling of muscle and connective tissue that suspends the front end of the horse's body, keeping it from falling down between its front legs. What? If you can picture the base of the horse's neck—the ribcage, withers, and back without the shoulder blades (scapula) or front legs attached—you might say the body is shaped somewhat like a canoe. Now imagine the legs and scapula as two tall posts with a net of super-strong rubber bands between them, and picture this canoe being held up by resting in this hammock, or sling. Notice that the boat is not nailed to the posts. For your horse, there is no bony connection (no joint) between the body and the limbs. Although you might think they couldn't be strong enough, the muscles and connective tissue are actually much better suited to support your horse's body between the front limbs than bone would be, because they have more flexibility to absorb the huge forces involved when the horse lands on the front feet. However, this is still quite a job and the pectorals do experience stress from it, particularly at greater speeds or over jumps, or when adding the weight of a rider. And this isn't the only job for the pectorals. They also move the forelimbs sideways, forward, and backward. You can see why many horses can get a bit defensive about having these muscles massaged.

Technique 5
Freeing the Breath

First make contact with your horse's shoulder or withers, and stroke from there down into the girth area just behind the elbow. Each of the following strokes will follow the line of the ribs, stroking from about the level of the horse's elbow up to the back muscles. The first of these up-strokes will be along the back of the shoulder, a little in front of where the saddle's girth would lie. The next strokes will each be a few inches further back, until you get to the last rib, or the flank area. See illustration on page 64.

Use the back of an open fist in contact with your horse's side. The other hand can fit inside the first hand. Using a moderate pressure, stroke slowly upward.

Take the stroke just past the top of the ribs into the back muscles. Notice my shoulders are still relaxed and down.

The last stroke follows the back of the last rib, a sensitive area for many horses. Using one hand is an option for any of the rib strokes, but it works especially well for this flank area.

Coaching Tips

1. Practice the same quality of adjusting speed and pressure as you did for the Deep Strokes and Strumming and Smoothing (techniques 3 and 4). One stroke might take anywhere from five seconds to several minutes, depending on how much pressure you're using and how your horse is responding. Making each stroke last three of your breaths is a good starting point.

2. Standing close for the beginning of the stroke when your hands are low, then stepping back a bit for the upper part, will help you work from your center with good body mechanics.

Anatomy: The Ribs

It's easy to remember the importance of mobility in the legs, back, and neck. We sure notice if they're not moving right because they have an obvious effect on how horses get around. Ribs, on the other hand, don't seem to move a whole lot anyway, so how could they be that important? Well for one thing, they share joints with the vertebrae in the back, so their movement, or lack of movement, impacts the joints of the spine very directly. Also, if your horse isn't able to breathe freely and deeply, not only will his strength and stamina be affected, but soon enough so will the health of any cell in the body that needs oxygen delivered to it. (And yes, that would be every cell in the body.) The mobility of your horse's ribs is vital to the health and comfort of the whole system. And the ribs have plenty of stresses to deal with. We and our saddles sit on them. We tighten girths around them. We challenge our horses mentally and emotionally at times, which can cause them to hold their breath (just like us). Other horses may kick them in the ribs. If they slip and fall, guess what they land on. And guess what tight muscles can pull them out of balance: not just rib muscles, but shoulder, hip, back, chest, stomach, pelvis, and neck muscles, too, all share attachments on the ribs.

Technique 6
Loosening the Glutes

The gluteal muscles, or glutes for short, are the large group of muscles across the top of the rump.

First you will use your hands much like a pushing a plow to rake across the muscles, loosening tensions and adhesions. Start each stroke near you and push, or plow, across the top of the rump toward the midline. Use both hands together to be kinder to your shoulders. You may also choose to use a stool for this technique. (See notes on safety regarding stools, page 41, and illustration on page 64.)

Then apply the same plow-like stroke in line with the muscle fibers. Keep wrists as straight as you can, with fingers in roughly the same line as the wrist but just slightly curved so the finger pads are the focus of contact. Think of this hand as a tool, and use the top hand to apply most of the pressure. See illustration on page 64.

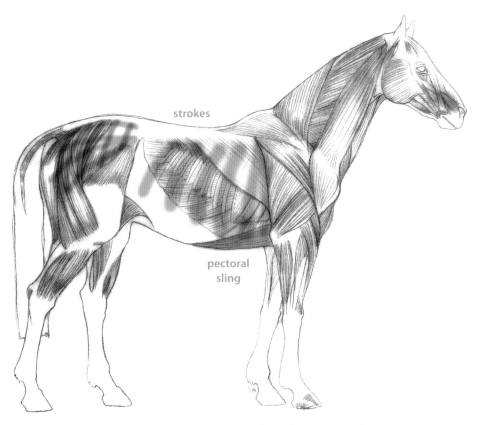

strokes

pectoral
sling

These lines indicate the strokes for techniques 5 and 6.

This is essentially the Strumming and Smoothing technique you used in the chest muscles, applied with different body mechanics and with the addition of a technique for reducing trigger points. A trigger point is one type of a point in a muscle that triggers a spasm or pain response. You may observe this by seeing muscles twitching, your horse sinking or moving away, or your horse looking worried, swishing his tail, etc. You may or may not feel a knot or adhesion at the trigger point. In any case, when you get a spasm or pain response, stop and repeat several strokes (three to five times) through the area, in line with the muscle fibers (see illustration), at a pressure and speed that your horse can tolerate. Trigger points often improve quite a bit with this technique. They can also benefit as releases happen in other areas of the body.

Move on and finish loosening the rest of the glutes. Follow with some effleurage strokes to soothe the area and help flush it with fluids to remove waste products.

Note: If the trigger points are still tender, there are additional approaches that you can learn more about in the resources listed at the back of this book and on the website, or you can learn directly from a professional. It is possible to overwork these painful points, so be sure you are well-informed as you proceed.

Coaching Tips

1.   Whenever you use your fingertips, do not hyperextend your joints (i.e., bend them backward). Keep your fingers straight or slightly curved.

2.   A good alternative to fingertips is to use one or more knuckles or the back of a fist.

Anatomy: Trigger Points

As you experience massage through receiving, reading, watching, and generally hanging out with massage-type folks, you will come across terms like trigger point, stress point, acupressure or acupuncture point, adhesion, knot, pressure point, or tender point, or, some of my favorite names, zingy, ouchy, and juicy points. These each have characteristics that define them (well, maybe the last three aren't so clearly defined) and can exist purely as one thing, but also often happen together at the same location. Many times you won't know exactly which definition(s) best apply, but you can still work with them productively with certain guidelines and experience.

For now, let's look briefly at trigger points. These occur in the middle part, or belly, of a muscle. They are generally, though not always, painful where the pressure is applied, but also refer pain to other areas that may seem quite unconnected. This is easily demonstrated in people, who can tell you where they feel the sensations when you press on a point. You may not know when your horse is experiencing pain referred to another location, but that doesn't mean she isn't.

Left untreated, a trigger point will become dehydrated, acidic, fibrous, and more painful. It can also eventually become less painful again as it becomes dormant (sleeping). However, even dormant trigger points interfere with function, both in strength and flexibility. That is, the muscle won't be used in its full range of motion (ROM), either in stretching or when contracting. And if one muscle is not able to do its full job, something else is going to have to take an extra load, whether that be another muscle or connective tissue or a joint.

Technique 7
Shoulder and Hip Circles

Note: If your horse is currently injured in any limb, be sure to ask your veterinarian when it would be appropriate to begin this technique.

This is a fantastic technique for both assessing and improving how your horse's shoulder and hip joints are moving. As you repeat the circles, you are stimulating joint fluid, which lubricates the joint, makes the movement more fluid and comfortable, and nourishes the cartilage, joint capsule, and ligaments. You also will be helping to balance the tensions of the muscles surrounding the joints, which keeps the joint better aligned, reducing stress and strain. As if these benefits aren't enough, you're also giving the nervous system positive input about joint range of motion through the proprioceptors in and around the joints.

Begin by picking up the hoof just as if you were going to clean it. Bend from the hips and keep your back as flat as you can, and resting one or both elbows on your thighs. You can also rest your horse's leg against your thigh.

Jostle the whole limb slightly to reduce muscle guarding and to stimulate joint fluid. Once you feel that your horse's leg is relaxed, slowly make small circles with it. Imagine a beam of light shining onto the ground through the knee (in front leg), or the toe or fetlock (in back). This beam of light will draw a circle on the ground under the shoulder or hip. Use your legs rather than your arms to create this motion, keeping at least one elbow on your thigh the whole time to support your back.

The hind leg here is on its way around a circle about as large as needed for the purposes of this technique. On the inside portion of this same circle the lifted hoof will pass right alongside the inside of the standing leg.

Make three to five circles in one direction, pause, then go the other way around for each leg. Watch for and encourage, but don't force, the circles to get a little bigger with each repetition. Also feel for the circles gliding more smoothly.

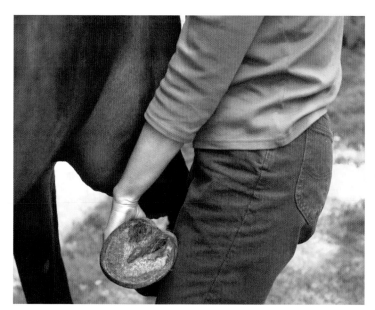

An option for the front leg, standing upright if this is better for your body. My right hand, not seen here, is supporting Kiona's forearm.

Coaching Tips

1. You can avoid resistance in your horse by not giving him anything to resist against. If he pulls his leg away, do not pull back but simply follow his motion till he relaxes again, then restart the jostles, then the circles.

2. If your horse objects to large circles, just keep them quite small, even an inch in diameter, and only increase the size as the joints and muscles loosen up. Any size circle will help relax muscles and stimulate joint fluid.

Anatomy: Joint Health

The joints we're most familiar with, including shoulders, hips, elbows, stifles, wrists, hocks, etc., as well as all the vertebral and rib joints along the spine, are all synovial joints (pronounced *sin-oh-vee-all*). This type of joint needs synovial fluid to lubricate the cartilage that covers and cushions the ends of the bones. We know that some horses stay much more comfortable into their later years than others do. And for any horse, some joints within the body stay much healthier than others. Why is that? Apart from possible genetic or nutritional issues, three main sources of stress to joints are concussion, lack of movement, and unevenness of pressures.

Concussion: The joints are well designed to handle normal concussion, but if there are excessive forces, or if they are quite repetitive, problems can develop.

Lack of Movement: Movement actually stimulates the joint to produce more synovial fluid, *and* makes it thinner and more slippery, like warm, runny oil versus cold, goopy oil. This means the joint is better lubricated, and therefore the cartilage is better protected from damage. When a joint moves less, these benefits don't happen. Lack of movement may involve the whole body, such as with confinement, or a single joint, due to tension, pain, injury, or habitual patterns.

Unevenness of Pressures: What if the bones are chronically more compressed on one side of a joint than the other? On the compressed side there's more pressure on the cartilage *and* less room for synovial fluid, so guess where the damage happens to cartilage? And on the other side of the joint, ligaments can be strained where they're being more stretched. Uneven pressures can have many causes, including conformation weaknesses, poor posture, or simply uneven muscle tensions.

Technique 8
Opening the Back

Starting each line next to the spine, lightly hook your finger pads into the muscle tissue and pull toward you, ending about the top of the ribs. Stand at an angle, facing your horse's opposite hip. This will make your strokes angled, too, as you bring them straight toward your body. As with Loosening the Glutes, think of your bottom hand as a tool and apply more of the pressure with the top hand. You can apply the strokes working forward from glutes to withers, or from withers to glutes. If you come across trigger points in the back, use the same instructions covered in Loosening the Glutes.

My right elbow is actually resting lightly on her back. Make it as easy on yourself as possible.

Coaching Tip

Don't zip too fast through the back muscles. They can have a healthy reflex response of flinching muscles, but are also often sore, tight, and full of trigger points. If you apply the strokes too fast, you can cause unnecessary additional pain, and also be less able to distinguish the pain response from a nerve reflex.

Anatomy: The Spine

Quite an area of interest for any horse lover, since a pain-free back is vital to the horse's happiness, soundness, and comfort. Let's look at how the health of the spine impacts the rest of the body, primarily in two ways: shock absorption and nerve communication.

Shock absorption: Although the horse's back is designed to be more stable and strong than flexible, the small ranges of flexibility it is meant to have are still vital. Considerable forces from landing on or pushing off from the ground travel up the legs and into the body. These forces must be transmitted *through* the back in order to be absorbed, utilized, and eventually dispersed appropriately. If the back is stiff and not able to allow this wave of energy to flow through, there will be more concussion (shock) into the joints and muscles of the back itself, and into the feet, limbs, hips, pelvis, shoulders, neck, and even the jaw. (Did I leave anything out?) If you have ever ridden a horse with a stiff back, you have felt this jarring result in your own body. For the horse to travel through her back, she must not only learn (by good training) and be assisted (by good riding) to use her whole body in a coordinated and efficient pattern, but she must also have joints and muscles that are physically able to respond in a healthy and functional way.

Nerve communication: Just like all the synovial joints in the body, the relatively small movements available in the spine contribute importantly to locomotion and soundness. But these vertebral joints also have something going on that other joints don't. They are located where nerves enter and exit the spinal cord. Any conditions such as reduced circulation, inflammation, and excessive or prolonged muscle tension around these joints are also creating extra pressures on these nerves. This can cause considerable pain, guarding, and tension. It also interferes with healthy nerve communication, which impacts coordination and athleticism, as well as potentially any of the organs (liver, heart, stomach, intestines, etc.). Although as we know the body is highly adaptable in handling and responding to stress, problems in the back do have an especially big impact on the whole system due to the fact that much of the central nervous system is housed here.

The back especially is subject to innumerable stresses, including problems with saddle fit or pads, rider issues, weaknesses due to conformation, shoeing and trimming factors, unbalanced posture and movements from compensating for other problems (such as lameness in a limb), and even the effects of gravity over time. All of these stresses can lead to poor health of the muscle tissues along the spine and compression and stress in the vertebral joints, which in turn lead to pain, stiffening, and further dysfunction. The horse's back is a subject that all horse lovers, and especially riders, would do well to study at every opportunity.

Technique 9
Wither Rock and Lift

This simple series of movements is especially valuable for maintaining, improving, and getting feedback on the health of your horse's back. The movements will be small, but the difference between a small movement and no movement can be huge. I like to use this technique after I ride even if that's all I have time for, since it leaves the horse's back in a healthy and open position. It's also useful before a ride, or anytime. We'll focus here on the wither area, but you can extend the moves all the way through the back.

Part 1: Wither Rock (Side to Side)

Curved fingers hook and pull withers toward you, creating a slight bend and twist in the spine.

Push away using heel of your hand.

These movements should be gentle and slow. The horse should be able to stay relaxed and just rock and sway a little as you encourage a repeated wave pattern side to side through the spine, from withers through the low back (loin). Doing this side-to-side movement is beneficial in itself, but will also enhance the effects for the next movement in part 2.

Part 2: Wither (and Belly) Lift

For this part you will encourage your horse to lift his withers and slightly round his back up toward the sky. This is important for several reasons. It stretches the back muscles and tones the abdominal muscles. It's also the movement that advanced riders seek from their horses because it enables the horse to work through his back, with all of the benefits discussed for the spine in Technique 8, Opening the Back.

Begin the wither lift by placing the finger pads of both hands together right on your horse's midline, about where a girth would lie. You can often feel a hollow spot here. Look up at the horse's back and withers as you think and lift up, using a tickling or scratching pressure with your fingers. As the horse lifts (or maybe not yet?), you can continue the tickling or pressure along the midline toward the belly, watching for the middle of the back and ribs to lift. If your horse has a sensitive belly, you can start with easy pressure, only getting more focused (nagging or tickling) as needed.

If your horse doesn't lift his back, you may add some pressure or change the angle more from finger pads to fingernails, but you don't need to get too aggressive. If it takes more than that to get the movement, you already have some good information that there's room for improvement. Watch for and expect improvement with repetition of the technique. Alternating with the side-to-side movements (part 1) often helps the results of the wither and belly lifts quite a bit.

Position of the back
before the lift.

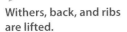

Withers, back, and ribs
are lifted.

Note: Be sure to watch carefully for signs of pain. If you are finding that these movements seem to be painful or are just not happening, it is probably time to call on a professional (veterinarian, bodyworker, chiropractor, acupuncturist, or all of the above). This could greatly speed up the process of getting your horse more comfortable and healthy, and may well be a necessary step.

Coaching Tips

1. When creating the side-to-side movements, the closer together your fingers or the heels of your hands are, the more you will focus joint movement into a smaller segment of the spine. To be quite thorough, use this approach. Or for a quicker, less focused application, you can have your pressure cover a longer segment of the spine.

2. As always, you must read your horse's feedback and know that yes indeed, he can reach your hand on his girth and belly with a kick quite easily. Respect his expressions and body language *before* you push him to protect himself. As with any of the techniques, you are responsible for knowing your horse and your level of experience to stay safe.

Anatomy: Transitions

What is going on during this Wither Rock and Lift, in addition to improving flexibility of the spine and engaging belly muscles? Let's look at the whole region below the wither, as it illustrates a major anatomy concept of transitions. Transition means change from one thing to another, which means temporarily less stability and more vulnerability in some form or fashion. (I'm sure you can see that this applies to more than just anatomy.) As a structure is transitioning from one shape or one type of tissue to another, it is more vulnerable to stresses and prone to developing problems. Examples include stress points in muscle tissue where muscle transitions to tendon, or a tendency to develop joint subluxations at transitions between segments of the spine (head to neck, neck to chest, mid-back to loin, loin to pelvis).

What transitions are happening physically in this region of the wither?

The limb (which includes the scapula, or shoulder blade) is transitioning onto the body. Remember from the information about the spine and the pectoral sling that great forces are being transmitted through this area from the ground into the back and to the rest of the body.

Under the withers and a bit forward, deep under the scapula, the neck is transitioning to the thorax, or body. As mentioned above, this segment of the spine is prone to joint subluxations and often benefits from the attention of a good chiropractor.

Just behind and below the highest part of the wither is the wither pocket, a relatively concave area behind the bulge at the top of the scapula. (If it's very concave, though, you might want to check whether your saddle is causing muscle atrophy here.) Even with a well-fitting saddle, this wither pocket and the portion of the back just behind it is the main area of transition between the saddle and rider and the horse's body. Clearly an area prone to some extra stress, whether from the saddle itself, the rider, or both.

Fortunately for your horse, this whole area, involving these many important transitions, benefits from the Wither Rock and Lift.

By now you have practiced all nine techniques taught in this chapter, and perhaps a number of variations of them as well. You may even have already begun to experiment with creating your own moves, which is a wonderful urge to follow. Are you noticing how much more awareness and understanding of your horse's body you are developing? And have you experienced any shifts in your relationship and communication yet? There is so much to learn and discover, and you are well on your way along this fulfilling and rewarding path. Congratulations! Now keep on massaging, and come visit us at *www.AllAboutAnimalMassage.com* to keep on learning.

An Invitation

All living beings are literal connections between Earth and Heaven. Earth, in this sense, is the physical, while Heaven is the life force, the soul. As long as there are living things, there is a union between the two. We and our animals are the embodiment of this relationship, and the healthier we are in body, mind, and soul, the stronger that connection is. Taking care of yourself is, therefore, an important commitment that benefits the world, not just yourself.

Also important is to contribute in some way to the health and well-being of others, including the animals in your life, just as you are doing now by learning about animal massage. I have chosen a specific focus for myself that many of you may share. Having spent a number of years volunteering for and eventually as an instructor with therapeutic riding centers, I have a special interest in the well-being of therapy animals. I have a specific vision that all horses serving people in therapeutic programs receive regular bodywork. This would be an important addition to the other forms of appreciation and attention they already receive from their riders, handlers, and care-givers. There are so many ways to contribute, whether by massaging, raising funds, organizing, educating, or inspiring. In fact, in buying this book and anything else from the website you are already contributing, as a portion of all proceeds are dedicated to promoting and providing massage and bodywork for therapy animals serving nonprofit organizations. Please visit my website *www.AllAboutAnimalMassage.com* for more information.

I hope you have found this book to be a valuable resource, raising your awareness of how the body works and responds to touch, and making the quality of the care you are able to provide the horses in your life even higher. I also hope you feel and believe, perhaps more than you did before, that you have great power to help the animals you love with massage!

Love,

Megan Ayrault

Megan's horse Rainbow invites you to check out the All About Animal Massage e-books for more massage techniques, including those especially loved by older animals.

Glossary

acupressure: use of pressure to stimulate acupoints along meridians to balance the flow of Chi energy

acupuncture: use of needles to stimulate acupoints along meridians to balance the flow of Chi energy

adaptation: changes in a living organism that help it cope with stresses and pressures

adhesion: abnormal binding together of tissues

bodywork: any therapeutic system of touch or manipulation for healing purposes, including massage, acupressure, chiropractic care, yoga, Rolfing, etc.

cartilage: fibrous, elastic tissue acting as a cushion at ends of bones

chiropractic adjustment: manipulation of a subluxated joint, or subluxation, by a chiropractor (see subluxation)

compensation: one or more structures of the body working harder or in a different way than normal in response to dysfunction in another structure or structures

concussion: impact of physical forces into joints and bones

conformation weakness: an aspect of an individual's structure that is more prone to stress and strain in bones, joints, or soft tissues

Craniosacral Therapy (CST): a system of bodywork addressing fascial restrictions and the movement of cerebral spinal fluid within the central nervous system from brain to sacrum (base of spine)

diagnosis: identification of a disease or condition by its symptoms and by diagnostic procedures

edema: excess fluid between cells; swelling

effleurage: a soothing massage stroke that warms surface tissues and stimulates blood flow

endorphins: compounds produced within the body that create a sense of well-being and reduce pain

farrier: a specialist in equine (horse) hoof care, including trimming and shoeing

fascia: a type of connective tissue forming membranes of varied thickness throughout the body

fetlock: a joint in the horse's leg just above the hoof

girth: both the area of the horse's body around the ribcage just behind the shoulder and the item of tack (equipment) that fits here to secure the saddle on the horse's back

gluteal muscles: the large, powerful group of muscles at the top of the horse's rump

hock: the equivalent of the human ankle; the joint in the hind leg above the fetlock and below the stifle

immune system: a combination of mechanisms of the body that work to prevent and fight disease

joint capsule: a tough membrane around the structures of a synovial joint containing the synovial fluid

knots: adhesions in soft tissue that can be felt as fibrous lumps

ligament: connective tissue bands connecting bone to bone

lymph, lymphatic fluid: fluid throughout the body that nourishes cells and transports waste products, white blood cells, and other molecules (some fats and proteins)

lymph nodes: small glands in the lymphatic system that filter lymph fluid and prevent infections from spreading

Manual Lymphatic Drainage: one of several names for a type of massage that focuses on stimulating the movement of lymphatic fluid to reduce edema and support the immune system

martingale: a piece of equipment used to control head height when riding or driving horses

modality: within the larger context of bodywork, each distinct type or system of therapeutic touch is a modality. Bodyworkers may be trained in one or multiple modalities.

muscle guarding: when a muscle tenses or holds in order to protect an area or prevent a movement

myofascia: the fascia within and surrounding a muscle (*myo* refers to muscle tissue)

Myofascial Release: may refer to a modality of bodywork in itself or a technique within other modalities. It improves the function and flexibility of fascia (especially, but not limited to, myofascia) by lengthening, hydrating, reducing adhesions, or unwinding. Unwinding is a term describing fascial release and reorganization, including emotional and positional (movement) releases.

palpation: use of feel to assess texture, temperature, tension, tenderness, and range of motion

parasympathetic system: part of the autonomic, or automatic, nervous system that triggers rest and relaxation responses in the body

patella: the kneecap

pectoral muscles: a group of chest muscles that support the body and move the front limbs

pectoral sling: a description of the fact that in quadrupeds (four-legged animals) the pectoral muscles help to suspend the front of the ribcage between the front legs

petrissage: variations of massage strokes that compress, knead, and wring muscle tissue, working deeper into the layers beneath the skin

physiology: the study of the functions of living organisms; how structures of the body work

prognosis: a prediction of how a condition or disease will progress

proprioception: the sense of the body's position in space, including the relative positions of different body parts to each other

range of motion: the movement available at any given joint

repetitive stress injury: an injury that results from the cumulative effect of a series of smaller stresses

scapula: the shoulder blade

Shiatsu: (*lit.*, finger pressure) a system of bodywork originating in Japan, based also, historically, on modalities from China; uses a combination of compression massage, acupressure, and stretches

stay apparatus: an organization of structures in the horse's legs that allows the horse to stand upright with little or no muscle effort

sternum: the breastbone in the center of the chest

stifle: the equivalent of the human knee; the joint in the hind leg below the hip and above the hock

stress point: usually located at the junction between muscle and tendon; an area of stress, pain, and dysfunction that responds well to massage

structural integration: a category of bodywork that uses soft tissue manipulation to realign the skeletal structure for better function and efficiency; includes Rolfing and its offshoots

subluxation: in the context of chiropractic care, a subtle misalignment of a joint that impacts the nervous system

sympathetic nervous system: part of the autonomic, or automatic, nervous system that triggers fight or flight responses in the body

synergistic: when the outcome, or whole, is greater than the sum of the parts

synovial joint: type of joint having a joint capsule containing synovial fluid, which lubricates and nourishes the cartilage of the joint

tapotement: a category of percussive (drum-like) massage strokes

tendon: tissue connecting muscle to bone

tensegrity: a term created to describe a synergistic balance of tension and compression, resulting in "tensional integrity"

toxin: a poisonous substance

trauma: a physical or emotional injury

triceps: the triangular-shaped muscle at the back of the shoulder that flexes (bends) the shoulder and extends (straightens) the elbow

trigger point: a sensitive point or nodule within a muscle that triggers a pattern of pain when pressure is applied

vertebra (singular), vertebrae (plural): irregularly shaped bones that join together to form the spine, including cervical (neck), thoracic (upper back), lumbar (lower back), sacral (base of spine), and coccygeal (tail bone) vertebrae

withers: the ridge between the shoulder blades; a segment of the horse's spine where the neck transitions into the back

Resources

To continue your education and inspiration, please visit *www.AllAboutAnimalMassage.com* for the following resources:

- Expert Advisory Board

- Free "All About Animal Massage" newsletter

- The "Animal Wellness Network"

- "Ask Megan" Animal Massage Blog

- Recommended books, videos/DVDs, e-books, and other products

- Workshops, webinars, and other events

- Schools offering training and certification

- Links to animal massage-related organizations and websites

- Research and other articles

- Find a professional in your area

- Support massage for therapy animals

- Video clips available for viewing

These many resources provide information and services covering a wide range of animal massage topics and related care, including:

- Massage for cats and other animals, as well as dogs and horses

- Massage for older animals, or those needing extra TLC

- Information on varieties of massage and bodywork

- Animal anatomy

- Animal massage regulations

- Chiropractic care

- Saddle fitting

- FAQs

Below are just a few examples of the many recommended books and videos available in our store at *www.AllAboutAnimalMassage.com*.

Books

Brennan, Mary L., DVM. *Complete Holistic Care and Healing for Horses.* North Pomfret, VT: Trafalgar Square Publishing, 2001.

Giniaux, Dominique, DVM. *What the Horses Have Told Me.* Middlehurst, OH: Xenophon Press, 1996.

Hannay, Pamela. *Shiatsu with Horses.* London: J.A. Allen, 1999.

Meagher, Jack. *Beating Muscle Injuries for Horses.* Hamilton, MA: Hamilton Horse Associates, 1985.

Wyche, Sara. *Muscles in Motion.* Wiltshire, Great Britain: The Crowood Press Ltd., 2002.

Videos

Harris, Susan, and Brown, Peggy. *Anatomy in Motion: The Visible Horse.* North Pomfret, VT: Trafalgar Square Publishing, 2000.

Michelin, Lola. *Large Animal Massage Demonstration (Horse).* Redmond, WA: Northwest School of Animal Massage, 2006.

Index

movement, 5–6, 9
    lack of, 68
    proprioception and, 17
muscle guarding, 55, 70, 80
muscles
    gluteal, 63–65, 69, 80
    pectoral, 57, 59, 64, 74, 80–81
    transitions and, 74
    triceps, 54–56, 82
    trigger points and, 65
Myofascial Release, 8, 17, 80

N
neck
    jostling, 52–53
    restraints and, 39
negative feedback, 38, 43–44, 53, 57, 59, 64, 74
nerve communication, 70
Neuromuscular Therapy, 8

O
observations, 37–39, 43–44
Opening the Back, 69–70, 72
organs and spine health, 70

P
pain, 16, 19, 37–38, 73
    riders and, 10
    trigger points and, 64–65, 70
palpation, 37, 80
parasympathetic mode (rest and relaxation), 14, 18, 80
    neck and, 53
patella, 55, 80
pectoral muscles, 57, 59, 64, 74, 80–81
petrissage, 81
petting, therapeutic, 43–44
physiology, 7, 9, 81
posture, 6
pressure
    stress and, 9–10
    uneven, 68
prognosis, 23, 81
proprioception, 17, 20, 66, 81

R
range of motion, 17, 20, 66, 81
    trigger points and, 65
reflexology, 8
regulations, 30
reins, 9–10
relationship
    between Heaven and Earth, 77
    between your horse and you, 6, 75
release, 37

repetitive stress injuries, 9, 20, 81
resistance, 68
resources, 2, 36, 45, 83–84
rest and relaxation (parasympathetic), 13–14
    immune system and, 18
    neck and, 53
restraining your horse, 39–40
restrictions, 13
    circulation and, 15
results of sessions, 26–28
ribs, 60–62, 68
riders, 59
    bodywork for, 29
    spine health and, 70
    stress and, 10
Rolfing, 8, 30
ropes, 40

S
saddles, 10, 74
safety, 39–43, 57
scapula, 59, 74, 81
scar tissue, 6
    circulation and, 15
    healing and, 20
sessions, creating, 47–48
    see also Techniques
Shiatsu, 29, 81
shock absorption, 70
shoulder, 54, 66–68
Shoulder and Hip Circles, 66–68
sleep, 6, 9, 56
social interaction, 9
spine, 70–74
    see also back
Sports Massage, 8, 29
stay apparatus, 55–56, 81
sternum, 57–58, 81
stess points, 13
stifle, 55–56, 68, 81
stool, standing on during massage, 41, 63
stress, 5–6, 9–11, 13–14
    spine health and, 70
stress point, 81
stretching, 48
Structural Integration, 8, 17, 29, 81
Strumming and Smoothing, 48, 57–59, 61, 64
subluxation, 10, 74, 81
surgery, 6, 9
swelling (edema), 6, 19
    effleurage and, 49
    lymphatic massage and, 18
sympathetic mode (fight or flight), 14, 81
synergism, 2, 81
synovial joints, 68, 70, 81